Avanke, Bever, Castor:

the story of

BEAVERS IN WALES

by Bryony Coles

*In Tivi above all the ryvers in Wales were
in Giraldus tyme a great numbre of castors,
which maye be Englished bevers,
and are called in Welshe avanke*

(Humphrey Llwyd 1559, ed. Ieuan Williams 2002)

WARP

Wetland Archaeology Research Project

Map of Wales showing beaver-related locations

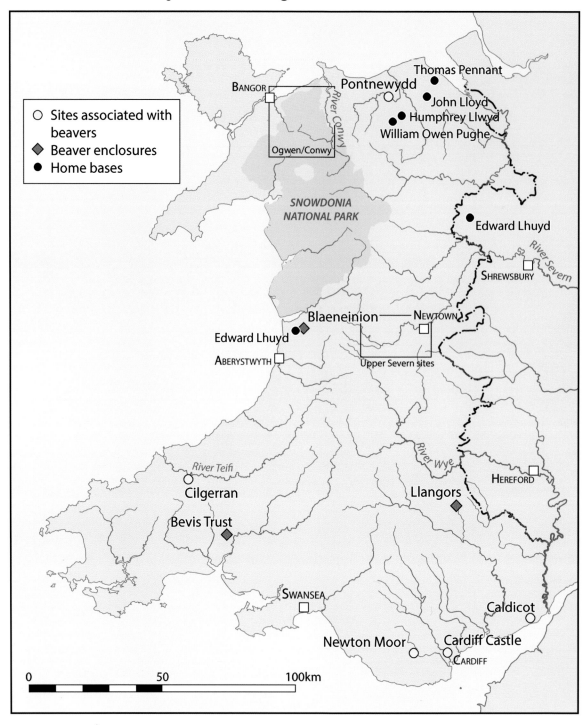

(Ogwen/Conwy and Upper Severn maps occur in Chapter 5)

Avanke, Bever, Castor

CONTENTS

Thomas Pennant (1726 – 1798)

William Owen Pughe (1759 – 1835) and oral traditions

A damper on the afanc

The Marquis of Bute and Cardiff Castle

Llyn yr Afangc, Afon Conwy
Conwy tributaries

Afon Ogwen, in Nant Ffrancon
The Ogwen and Conwy catchments

Finding Llyn yr Afangc in Montgomeryshire

Pwll Lostlydan, Radnorshire (Powys)

Place-names and beaver features

The character of the evidence

The evidence in space and time

Return of the beavers

Restoration of the landscape

Preface and Acknowledgements

This, my second book about beavers, is a development from the first, *Beavers in Britain's Past*, which itself grew out of many years of work with my husband John Coles in the Somerset Levels. It was in the Levels that I first came across beaver-gnawed wood, preserved for millennia in the waterlogged peats, and I realised that beavers were not simply story-book creatures or providers of hats, but animals once native to Britain. The research that followed included fieldwork in beaver territories in mainland Europe, mainly in France where, unlike so many other European countries including Britain, beavers had not become extinct.

Several seasons of fieldwork in Brittany and in south-east France (the Beaver Works Project) proved an eye-opener in terms of the variety of places where beavers settled, and their ecological significance, in addition to providing evidence for the wide range of beaver activities that could leave traces for an archaeologist to find. But where to start looking for new evidence in Britain? After completing *Beavers in Britain's Past*, I soon decided on a further project in Wales, thanks to the combination of beaver-related place-names, historical records relating to beavers, and the lure of the landscapes to be explored. In 2008 a Small Research Grant from the British Academy enabled several fieldwork sessions, alongside research in a range of libraries and archives. There was then a hiatus in my work on beavers in Wales, for various reasons, and when I returned to it much had changed in terms of public awareness of beavers. Throughout Britain, people had become more aware of beavers as a native species, adept in environmental engineering, a development which encouraged me to complete the book. It has happily become part ecology, part archaeology and part history, a mixture that I had hoped for at the outset, but wasn't sure of achieving. In addition, the future of beavers throughout Britain has become as important as their past.

Some caveats: Firstly, I have not attempted to cover every beaver-related place name in Wales nor every historical record, but what follows is, I hope, representative of the known evidence. Secondly, spellings of certain words have varied over time, and the most variable are the beaver's Welsh name 'afanc' and the surname 'Llwyd'; I have tried to be consistent in using the spelling most appropriate to the context. Thirdly, it may be due to my training as a prehistorian that I have made frequent use of words such as 'possibly', 'probably', 'perhaps', 'maybe' and other words of caution. Discoveries of new evidence and the development of new techniques for studying it are likely to change the picture drawn here, and that is all to the good. One thing I am sure of, that there is beaver-related evidence still to be found and understood, and perhaps this book will prompt readers to look for it.

There are many people to thank for their contributions. Adam Wainwright and Chris Smart (University of Exeter) both assisted in the early stages of identifying sources and making contacts, while Astrid Caseldine (Cadw), Elizabeth Walker (National Museum Wales) and others, have several times checked their records for archaeological traces of beavers in Wales, and confirmed that few have been reported to date. In addition to the British Academy grant, fieldwork was facilitated by Environment Agency staff from Bangor, especially Janet Buckles, and by National Trust staff including Dewi Roberts. John Coles has helped with all the practicalities of map reading and recording, particularly during the fieldwork.

In the early stages, Ceri Davies and Nancy Edwards helped with historical references, as did Eva and Nick Moore. Iwan ap Dafydd of the National Library of Wales provided advice and assisted with illustrations, Robin and Pamela Wootton foraged in the heights and the bowels of the library of the Devon and Exeter Institution to find copies of Thomas Pennant's work, and Lynda Brooks of the Linaean Society Library helped with John Ray's works. Librarians in the British Library, the Wellcome Institution and the Society of Antiquaries of London have also been generous with their time and advice, while Matthew Williams guided me around the beavers of Cardiff Castle. The translation of the captions into Welsh has been done efficiently and speedily by Haf Roberts.

In addition, I acknowledge material from Professor Melville Richards's place-name research archive deposited at the University of Wales Bangor, accessed through the Archif Melville Richards database (AMR), a project funded by grants from the University of Wales Board of Celtic Studies and the Arts and Humanities Research Board.

My thanks go also to the beaver experts who have shared their knowledge and attempted to answer my questions, including Peter Burgess, Roisin Campbell-Palmer, Paul Chanin, Mark Elliott, Derek Gow, Duncan Halley, Adrian Jones, Simon Jones, Alicia Leow-Dyke and Göran Sjöberg.

Many of the photographs come from my own fieldwork projects, in Wales and beyond. However, the photos of live beavers are all taken in Britain, either in south-west England or in Wales – I didn't even dream this would be possible at the outset, and my thanks to the Devon Wildlife Trust and the Welsh Beaver Project for providing the photos. The maps have been drawn by Sean Goddard, a great improvement on my sketches. The diagrams were drawn by Mike Rouillard, initially for *Beavers in Britain's Past*. Other images have been supplied with speed and efficiency by the Tate, Science Museums, University of Wales Library, National Museum Wales and the Centre for Advanced Welsh and Celtic Studies, and further details are included in the relevant captions.

I owe a great debt to the readers of the first draft of the book, environmental archaeologists, medieval archaeologists and historians, and ecologists, for their keen eyes in spotting minor errors and especially for their comments and corrections with regard to various aberrations, and their suggestions of additional relevant material. They are Martin Bell, Tony Brown, John Coles, Nancy Edwards, Adrian Jones, Alicia Leow-Dyke and Huw Pryce, and I thank them all for saving me from several pitfalls, and greatly enhancing the overall story. Throughout I have been encouraged by John's wisdom, curiosity and sense of humour.

Finally my thanks to Hedgerow Print Ltd., for turning my text and images into this book.

CHAPTER 1

THE ECOLOGY AND ARCHAEOLOGY OF BEAVERS

Introduction

Beavers are known to have been present in Wales for as long as humans, and it is likely that they had at least as much influence as humans on the Welsh landscape. Yet, for all the many millennia that the beavers have been here, there is relatively little direct evidence for them, in marked contrast to the vast and varied range of information relating to humans. Nevertheless, there are clues, and in the first part of this book I will use both archaeological and documentary evidence to piece together the early history of beavers in Wales. From the Tudor period onwards, the evidence becomes more challenging, and its interpretation has proved controversial, particularly in relation to the timing of beaver extinction. My argument here will favour a late extinction date, and an enduring cultural interest in beavers, based on a combination of place-name evidence and recent discoveries.

An overview of the combined evidence then provides the framework for looking at the implications of returning beavers to Wales, as a wild population contributing to future developments across a range of natural habitats. It is only recently, as beavers have begun to expand from their refuge areas in Europe, and in North America, that humans have been able to study their influence on their surroundings, and to appreciate how significant and valuable that can be, not just for the beavers but also for humans and many other species. Beavers are recognised as a keystone species, and we are beginning to understand how they enrich the environment, enabling more species of plants and animals to flourish. They are also, as expert water engineers, relevant to the management of water in the landscape, and their presence and activities can mitigate both flood and drought. In this short book, I hope

Fig. 1.1 A female beaver with two kits, sitting in shallow water beside a Devon river. One of the female's nipples can be seen (below front foot, between the kits) suggesting she is still feeding her young. *Photo Mike Symes, Devon Wildlife Trust.*

Ffigur 1.1 Afanc benywaidd gyda dau o rai bach yn eistedd mewn dŵr bas wrth ymyl afon yn Nyfnaint. Mae un o dethi'r fenyw i'w gweld (o dan y droed dde, rhwng y ddau genau), gan awgrymu ei bod yn dal i fwydo ei rhai bach. *Llun Mike Symes, Ymddiriedolaeth Natur Dyfnaint.*

to introduce readers to the nature and history of beavers and to provide information relevant to their potential re-establishment in the Welsh landscape.

The European beaver, *Castor fiber* (Fig. 1.1) is a mammal belonging to the order Rodentia, sub-order Sciuromorpha, family Castoridae, the other living member of the family being *Castor canadensis*, which is native to North America. Throughout this book, 'beaver' refers to *Castor fiber* unless otherwise specified.

Beavers and their habitats

Much of this section on beavers and their habitats is based on my own fieldwork in western Europe, and it draws also on Andrew Kitchener's *Beavers* (2001) and *The Eurasian Beaver* by Roisin Campbell-Palmer and colleagues (2015).

Beavers, which are primarily nocturnal, live in family groups consisting of an adult pair and their offspring of the current and previous year, usually about five to eight individuals all told. They are semi-aquatic, living beside freshwater ranging from the relatively still conditions of lakes and large ponds to lowland rivers to fast running mountain streams. Beavers in winter live mainly off the twigs and bark of trees such as willow, aspen, poplar, ash and hazel. In summer, they add a variety of herbaceous plants to their diet. They make underground dens in river banks, reached by a burrow with an underwater entrance, which gives them protection from most predators. If there is not enough bank height for a dry den within the ground, they make a heap of wood and mud and stones, with a hollowed-out den within it reached by one or more burrows. As in North America, the above-ground den is generally known as a lodge (Fig. 1.2). If they settle on smaller rivers and streams where there is not enough depth of water to protect the burrow entrances, beavers build a dam to raise the water level, thereby often creating a pond behind the dam and sundry side-channels around the dam, and they may also build dams on minor trickles of water, to provide safe swimming routes (Fig. 1.3).

One beaver family may occupy 500m to 1500m or more of water's edge, depending on local conditions especially food supply, and within their territory they will have a number of burrows and dens, and perhaps six to ten dams if they have settled on a small, shallow watercourse. Their presence is likely to lead to a number of local changes, some immediately apparent, others more subtle, and in general tending to be less obvious as time goes by. Each complex of dam and pond acts as a nutrient and silt trap, leading to an increase in plant and animal life, both in terms of biomass and in the range of species present. There will be a great variety of water: still and maybe deep ponds behind the dams, water flowing fast over a part of the dam or in bypass channels around the ends, canals leading across the valley floor to feeding areas, and wet marshy ground around the ponds. In addition, there will be more underground water, along burrows and tunnels, and a raised water table. Insects, molluscs, amphibians, fishes and waterfowl benefit from this variety

Fig. 1.2 a) A beaver lodge in Brittany. Beavers enter their lodges from under water, and the above-ground structure has no visible entrance.

Ffigur 1.2 a) Gwâl afanc yn Llydaw. Mae afancod yn mynd i mewn i'w gwâl o dan y dŵr ac nid oes gan y strwythur sydd uwch ben y ddaear unrhyw fynedfa weladwy;

Fig. 1.2 b) a lodge on a sloping bank in south-east France, with a quantity of wood extending into the water, where it will keep fresh and provide winter food.

Ffigur 1.2 b) gwâl ar lan afon ar lethr yn ne ddwyrain Ffrainc, gyda rhywfaint o bren yn ymestyn i'r dŵr, lle bydd yn cadw'n ffres ac yn darparu bwyd ar gyfer y gaeaf.

Fig. 1.3 a) A beaver dam on a small stream in Brittany, built with uprooted flag-iris, wood and mud. Water trickles over, through, and around both ends of the dam, which retains a deep pool.

Ffigur 1.3 Argae afanc ar nant fechan yn Llydaw, wedi'i greu gyda gellesg, pren a mwd. Mae dŵr yn diferu dros, drwy ac o amgylch dau ben yr argae, sy'n cynnal pwll dyfn.

Fig. 1.3 b) a beaver canal, dammed just enough to provide a swimming route; the drop to the stream is about one metre.

Ffigur 1.3 b) camlas afanc, gyda'r argae'n ddigon i ddarparu llwybr nofio; mae'r gwymp i'r nant yn rhyw un metr.

Fig. 1.4 Dam across the river Ellez in Brittany. This dam is often washed out by high waters, and in due course rebuilt by the beavers.

Ffigur 1.4 Argae ar draws afon Ellez yn Llydaw. Mae'r argae yma'n cael ei olchi i ffwrdd gan ddŵr mawr yn aml ond yn cael ei ailadeiladu wedyn gan afancod.

Fig. 1.5 Mountain stream in south-east France, fed largely by snow melt and dammed by a beaver family.

Ffigur 1.5 Nant yn y mynydd yn ne ddwyrain Ffrainc, yn cael ei bwydo'n bennaf gan eira'n toddi a theulu o afancod yn creu argae arni.

of water, as do their predators, while many other species of animal come to feed off the enhanced vegetation, and to drink at the pools. Rivers up to about 15m wide may also be dammed (Fig. 1.4); the dam may not survive the strength of the river in flood, but usually it will be repaired when needed.

Most beaver territories can develop into wooded areas, contrary perhaps to our current human expectations. This is partly because trees too benefit from the increase in water and nutrients. In addition, an established beaver territory is likely to have well-developed patches of bushy growth, known as beaver pasture, which have developed from the stumps of trees and shrubs initially felled for food, and which now provide bark and twigs and leaves for the beavers to browse, thus reducing their need for further tree-felling.

As mentioned above, beavers are today regarded by ecologists as a keystone species, due to the extent to which they enhance their habitat, particularly where they build dams. In terms of understanding the former natural environments of Wales, it is therefore relevant to suggest that wherever beavers settled along streams and small rivers, and built dams, there will have been a greater mass and diversity of plant and animal life, than one might otherwise have expected. Along the lowland streams, territories may have been stable for numerous beaver generations. In the hills and mountains, the force of water following storms and seasonal snow-melt will often have broken any beaver dams, but I am sure there were dams there to be broken – and later re-built. In Europe as well as in North America, there are beaver territories along many mountain streams, including one which the Beaver Works Project team (see below) recorded in recent years, at an altitude of 800m on the southern edge of the Vercors plateau in southeastern France (Fig. 1.5).

Here, the beavers had built three dams, one at least 34m long, despite the overall steep gradient and huge force of water. The beavers had chosen a relatively quiet stretch of the stream, where the fall was below the average within the territory. The main dam broke soon after our first recording, but a few years later the beavers were still present, and they had begun to enlarge an upstream dam instead (Coles 2006, 27 & 158). In Wales, taking Snowdon for comparison with its peak just over 1000m high, one might imagine beaver territories in the valleys below the peak, for example at an altitude of about 450m where Llyn Llydaw reservoir is now. Under such conditions, or where food is less than plentiful, beavers are likely to shift to new territories after a few years, while other beavers may in due course settle in the abandoned areas. Cold winters would be no deterrent, as beavers can live for several months under ice, feeding off the bark from twiggy wood which, in the autumn, they stored underwater in the base of their pond. It is therefore possible to suggest that, if one were to trace out all the streams of Wales, it would soon become apparent that beaver-enhanced habitat could have occurred throughout the country, along the smaller watercourses. Its character would have fluctuated with the coming and going of the beaver population, but for contemporary humans and other species it would rarely have been out of reach.

The above scenario depends on another factor, however, and that is the density and distribution of the beaver population. From the late Middle Ages onwards, as the beaver populations of Europe shrank under pressure from ever-increasing human predation, they mainly survived where they could be at their most inconspicuous. Their territories were established along deep, slow-flowing rivers with well-vegetated surrounds, and perhaps in the larger swamps and marshes, where they had no need to fell trees or to build dams. In these circumstances, their impact on their surroundings was at its lowest, and most humans in Europe were probably unaware of their presence. Their final refuge areas were in northern and southern Norway, in Germany on the river Elbe, and in France in the lower catchment of the Rhône. In a few instances, the beavers may have survived in the uppermost reaches of a catchment, isolated and relatively undisturbed by humans.

The early 20th century recovery of beavers across Europe, stimulated by protective legislation, was barely noticed to begin with, a slow expansion from the lowland refuge areas for several decades, with some re-location by humans, followed by a more obvious spread during the second half of the 20th century. The pattern suggests that they first colonised the larger rivers and lakes where dams were not needed, and moved into the smaller watercourses only as population density increased. How it is that a young beaver pair suddenly starts to build dams, when for generation upon generation their ancestors have done no such thing, is another matter, but the fact is that they do.

For Wales, in the light of these broad trends it can be suggested that, for much of the time since the last retreat of the ice sheets, beavers were settled along most watercourses, with considerable influence on the immediate surroundings of the smaller watercourses. A retreat to the larger rivers and remote valleys perhaps set in by the late first millennium AD, and thereafter beaver influence was less apparent, and their presence less obvious to humans.

The Beaver Works Project

I first became interested in the story of beavers in Britain in the mid-1980s, a time when most people, myself included, knew very little about the habits and habitats of European beavers. Nor was much known about what sort of evidence they might leave behind. I did know, however, that archaeologists could not always distinguish beaver-gnawed wood from humanly-worked wood, because I had had that problem myself with some well-preserved Neolithic wood. I was also aware that beavers might make accumulations of wood that could be mistaken for the results of human activity, and that European beavers did sometimes build dams and create narrow canals, which an archaeologist might mistake for the work of humans. All of this came about through working with John Coles on the prehistoric archaeology preserved in the peats of the Somerset Levels and Moors, in the 1970s and 1980s. The wooden trackways and platforms which people had built in the marshlands from about 3800 BC onwards sometimes included wood with unusual cut-marks, which we eventually identified as beaver gnawing. We then found that one of the platforms on the marshland edge, which included a quantity of beaver wood, had within it the remains of a possible beaver lodge or food store. At the same time, the associated palaeo-environmental evidence from pollen and macro-plant remains and insects hinted at beaver activity affecting the local water levels and vegetation.

Fig. 1.6 Beaver Works Project, team at work
Ffigur 1.6 Prosiect Gwaith Afancod, y tîm ar waith

We began to look at the reports from other prehistoric wetland sites, and found descriptions of several features that could have been due to beavers, as well as an actual piece of beaver-gnawed wood, previously unrecognised as such, from the early Mesolithic site of Star Carr in Yorkshire. I decided that research on beavers from an archaeological point of view might be worthwhile, particularly as European beavers were expanding from their refuge areas and could be studied in the wild, in a variety of different environments. The Beaver Works Project (Fig. 1.6) grew from a short preliminary visit to the beavers in the Rhône valley to four years of seasonal survey in the contrasting environments of inland Finistère in the northwest of France and the Drôme region of southeastern France, with subsequent short spells in Poland, Denmark, Sweden and the Netherlands. The results are outlined here; for further detail see *Beavers in Britain's Past* (Coles 2006).

For the major field surveys in France, funded by the Arts and Humanities Research Fund, the British Academy, the Leverhulme Trust, the Natural Environment Research Council and the University of Exeter, several beaver territories were recorded in detail. A team of six to eight people, attuned to working in waterlogged conditions, made maps showing all the main visible features such as dams and lodges and activity areas, and larger-scale plans of individual dam complexes with associated canals and paths. We made extensive photographic records, and returned to some areas season after season to monitor the changes that were taking place. From the start, we found there was much more to record than we had anticipated, especially for the stream-based territories, including the abundant wildlife, both plants and animals, and the skilful beaver manipulation of water within their territories. At times we were overwhelmed with data, but gradually the different aspects fitted together within the framework of a beaver-enhanced ecosystem. We realised, for example, that the dam which raised water levels to protect a burrow entrance also trapped silts and nutrients from local run-off after the rains, which in turn benefited the trees and shrubs along the bank, while within the pond aquatic plants and animals increased in bulk and variety, and other animals came to feed off them. Sometimes, when we began work in the mornings, we would see the tracks of wild pig and deer that had visited overnight, or a heron would flap away as we approached, and sometimes a shy water-rail could be heard among the tangled vegetation round an old lodge. Planning a lodge, we might find signs that otters and water-voles had made use of it, as well as the beavers who built it, and when planning a dam, on the upstream side there might be large fish swimming around our waders, while small fry sheltered in the brushwood network of the downstream front of the dam. Everywhere there was the movement and sound of water, and a gentle background noise of life.

A number of the illustrations in this book derive from the Beaver Works Project, and I owe much of my understanding of beavers to the Project team, and to the knowledgeable people who introduced me to particular beaver territories and described the changes that had taken place since the beavers arrived.

Sources of evidence for the former presence of beavers

The physical evidence that indicates beavers were once present comes mainly from their bones and from beaver-gnawed wood. Beaver bones are solid and strong, likely to survive well in favourable burial conditions, and the skulls, jawbones and teeth in particular are distinctive enough for relatively easy identification, so the chances are that archaeologists and other interested people will correctly record their presence once found. In the archaeological record for beavers, bones are the most common type of evidence (see Catalogue in Coles 2006). However, bone survival depends on soil conditions, and relatively little has been found in Wales. Wood gnawed by beavers (Fig. 1.7) carries distinctive tooth marks, usually as groups of facets on the severed end, also as twirl-marks on a branch peeled of its bark, and sometimes as deeper gouges caused in debarking or in manipulating a piece of wood. Archaeologists familiar with beaver-gnawed wood have recognised it from a number of recently excavated sites, usually in wetland contexts. In recent years, most new finds of beaver evidence have consisted of gnawed wood. Much must have gone unrecognised in the past, when people in Britain and western Europe were generally unaware of beavers and did not know what their gnawed wood looked like.

Fig. 1.7 Examples of wood gnawed by beavers, showing their distinctive tooth marks.
Ffigur 1.7 Esiamplau o bren wedi'i gnoi gan afancod, yn dangos olion nodedig eu dannedd

Other tangible evidence comes from the remains of beaver structures, namely their dams and lodges. In wetland conditions, such structures have as much chance of surviving as humanly-built ones but, as with beaver-gnawed wood, people have only recently come to realise that beaver structures may have been present. What is more, there was a widespread belief in recent centuries that European beavers, unlike those of North America, did not build dams and lodges; this lessened still further any expectation of finding them in the archaeological record. Beaver features, such as burrows, dens (Fig. 1.8) and canals, may also survive in recognisable form. The potential for their survival in Wales is good, and they are further discussed below (Chapter 5). More problematic, in terms of recognition, are the changes in watercourse character due to beavers, and the sediments that accumulate in beaver ponds, but this is an area where further research on modern beaver activity in Europe may help in the identification of past activity in Wales.

Historical evidence likewise comes in various forms, mainly through the written word, also through depictions such as carvings and paintings. There has long been controversy over the reliability and significance of some of the historical texts relating to beavers and, as we shall see later, it continues today, especially in relation to the date of beaver extinction. The strongest historical evidence comes in the form of written accounts of beaver presence, and Wales has an outstanding example of this type with the description provided by Gerald of Wales (Giraldus Cambrensis) discussed in Chapter 3. Laws provide other written evidence, and there is further indirect evidence from the spoken word, as recorded in oral traditions and place-names. Overall, the Welsh written record reveals a strong and enduring cultural interest in beavers.

All of this material, like that from archaeology, requires careful evaluation before use in building up a picture of beavers and their interactions with humans over the generations. What follows is an attempt to do this for Wales, from the earliest evidence to the time of beaver extinction.

Den in bank

Den moved up to keep above rising water level

Water level rises further den moved above ground

Fig. 1.8 Development from underground den to above ground lodge.
Ffigur 1.8 Datblygiad o'r twll o dan y ddaear i wâl uwch ben.

CHAPTER 2

THE PREHISTORIC EVIDENCE FROM WALES

For the prehistoric period, before the arrival of the Romans in Wales, the evidence for beavers comes in physical form. At present, it consists of beaver bones and beaver-gnawed wood. There are some hints of former beaver structures and features, and the potential is high for future discoveries of this type of evidence, but at present the story relies on bone and wood and begins, as we shall see, with some teeth. Skeletal remains of European beavers are known from Britain from the late Pliocene onwards, more than 2.5 million years ago, when they co-existed with *Trogontherium*, the Giant Beaver. The following geological era, the Pleistocene, is characterised by repeated glaciations and during the coldest phases beavers, like all other mammals including humans, retreated from northwestern Europe to the warmer south. As conditions warmed up, first those plants and animals adapted to tundra conditions spread northwards again, followed by species of parkland and temperate forest. Beavers will survive in sub-arctic conditions, so long as they have a large enough underwater store to provide bark to eat during the long winters – their pond may be iced over, but they can dive from their den to the store which they built up in the autumn. Where temperate conditions are established, they will flourish. Life in Wales will have been possible for beavers in all but the coldest phases.

Pontnewydd and the Ice Age

In Wales the earliest known beaver evidence comes from Pontnewydd cave, about eleven kilometres inland of the present coast of North Wales (see Frontispiece map).

Today the cave looks down on Afon Elwy, flowing past from west to east and soon to join Afon Clwyd north of Llanelwy/St Asaph. The deposits in the cave have been investigated at various times since the later 19th century, and from the late 1970s the cave has been studied as part of the *Palaeolithic Settlement of Wales* research project led by the late Stephen Aldhouse-Green of the National Museums and Galleries of Wales (now known as National Museum Wales). This most recent work has brought the cave to international renown, in part through identification of the presence of humans, early Neanderthals, some 225,000 years ago. The human evidence, along with that for many other species, is largely fragmentary and best accounted for as deposited by natural processes, such as debris flow into the cave, rather than indicating purposeful occupation of the cave (Green 1984; Aldhouse-Green, Petersen and Walker 2011).

The beaver remains are mostly from contexts contemporary with the human evidence, but this does not necessarily mean the humans brought the beavers into the cave. The bones of other mammals found with the beavers are mainly from wolf and bear, with a few specimens from other species, suggesting an open woodland environment. The bears may have been living in a newly-discovered part of the cave system, and it is just possible that the beavers too were cave-dwellers; they sometimes tuck themselves away in small cavities within these natural shelters, rather than digging out an underground den or building a lodge. Beavers will swim along flooded underground tunnels to their cave dens (Coles 2006; Érome 1982), and they would not necessarily have been in direct competition with the bears for space, nor prey to the much larger omnivores. However, the identified beaver remains are from debris flow, a liquefied landslide carrying all sorts of things collected on its passage, which came to rest in the cave. This means that the part of the cave where the beaver remains were found is unlikely to have been where the beavers had their den.

The Pontnewydd beaver remains are all teeth, two incisors and nine molars. In life, beavers have two upper incisors and two lower incisors, together with one pre-molar and three molars on each side of both upper and lower jaw; beavers use their incisors to cut through wood, whether severing a small branch or biting into and eventually through a larger branch or trunk and then severing the topwood from the fallen stem. They carry away the wood which, if small enough in diameter, can be lodged in their mouth in the gap between incisors and cheek teeth. Bigger pieces may be gripped between incisors and forepaws and towed or dragged away. Bark is peeled away from stems and trunks using the incisors; small stems are held in the forepaws for peeling, and twirled, leaving a distinctive pattern of tooth marks at right angles to the long axis of the stem. In addition, incisors are an effective weapon in fights with other beavers, or in defence against predators. The cheek teeth are used to grind up leaves, twigs, bark and other woody matter into small and relatively digestible fragments. Humans have in the past used beaver teeth singly or still in the mandible as wood-working tools, incisors as chisels or gouges, and molars as rasps or planes.

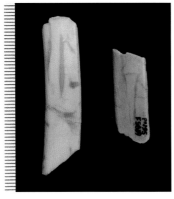

Fig. 2.1 The beaver incisors from Pontnewydd Cave (c. 250,000 years ago).

Ffigur 2.1 Blaenddannedd afanc o Ogof Pontnewydd (tua 250,000 o flynyddoedd yn ôl).

Beaver teeth grow in length and width throughout the individual's life, and they are continually being worn down and the incisors re-sharpened. In general, the bigger the teeth the older the beaver. Stefen, in a recent analysis of the variability in size of beaver teeth across species and through time, has concluded that beavers cannot be precisely aged by tooth size, but she does provide a general guide for *Castor fiber* (Stefen 2009). Incisors increase in width from 4 - 6mm in juveniles (0 - 12 months) to 8 - 9mm at fifty months or four years. From four to eighteen years the width is generally in the 9 - 10mm range.

The Pontnewydd teeth include two quite large fragments of incisor (Fig. 2.1). Both incisors are 9mm wide across the external enamel face, indicating that they probably come from one or two adult beavers, rather than from juveniles or sub-adults. The incisor on the left survives as a fragment 39mm long, creamy ivory in colour with blue-grey streaks and slight orange mottling. The shape of the fragment suggests it was a left lower incisor (Fig. 2.2a and 2.2b). The incisor on the right survives as a fragment 14mm long, and it too is likely to be a lower left incisor, but in this case bright orange in colour. The probable presence of two lower left incisors suggests the Pontnewydd teeth come from at least two adult beavers.

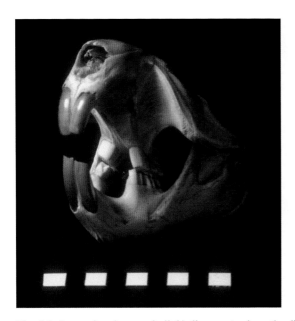
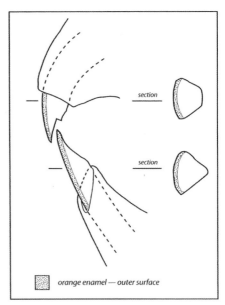

Fig. 2.2 a) a modern beaver skull; b) diagram to show the differences between upper and lower incisors. *Incisor photo courtesy of Amgueddfa Cymru - National Museum Wales.*

Ffigur 2.2 a) penglog afanc modern; b) diagram i ddangos y gwahaniaethau rhwng y blaenddannedd uchaf ac isaf. *Llun o'r blaenddant drwy garedigrwydd Amgueddfa Genedlaethol Cymru.*

Although many of the associated mammalian remains have an orange mottling and sometimes what looks like a patchy surface film of orange, in this instance the colouring has every appearance of being the original bright orange of beaver incisors in life. Of the beaver incisors from more recent archaeological contexts that I examined for *Beavers in Britain's Past,* relatively few retained their original orange colour, and no obvious correlation could be identified between time elapsed since death and preservation of colour.

Preparation of a beaver skull complete with teeth, for display purposes, has made me aware that boiling removes much of the orange colour of the incisors, but in the case of Pontnewydd there is no suggestion that the contemporary humans were boiling up bones. For the Pontnewydd beaver incisors, burial conditions are likely to be the governing factor, and it may have been a difference in conditions prior to the debris flow that caused the loss of colour for one incisor and its preservation for the other.

The nine cheek teeth are preserved to their full width, which ranges from 7mm to 10.5mm; this suggests the Pontnewydd cheek teeth are from well-grown individuals, though not necessarily all fully adult. Several retain their original very smooth, worn grinding surface.

As a group, the teeth from the cave carry some remarkably well-preserved detail. Although a beaver skeleton in general and the skull and teeth in particular are very dense and strong and often survive in good condition, the high degree of preservation at Pontnewydd indicates that the teeth were not exposed to weathering for any length of time. Nor were they subject to lengthy or severe mechanical action during the debris flow which carried them to where they were found, which suggests this process moved them only a short distance. Probably the beavers came from a nearby territory on the banks of the Elwy, and maybe they had a den in the cave system or were carried there by one of their several predators, such as a wolf.

Beavers at the end of the Ice Age?

For many millennia following the Pontnewydd occupation, direct evidence for beavers is strictly speaking absent from Wales, but a case can be made for their presence during the late Palaeolithic. During the coldest phase of the most recent glaciation, from about 20,000 to 15,000 years ago, conditions in Britain were too severe for beavers to live here, and for humans too. After 15,000 years ago, the climate began to ameliorate and from about 13,500 to 11,000 years ago more temperate conditions were established. This warm period of about 2,500 years is known as the Windermere interstadial, and it was long enough for both beaver and human populations to spread northwards across the landmass of Europe, reaching what was then the northwestern corner of the mainland, but is now the island of Britain. Beaver expansion followed that of their food sources, mainly willow and aspen during the early stages of the northwards spread, and their paths were the fresh-water rivers and streams of Europe. Watercourses and beaver ponds were maybe still frozen in winter, but beavers are known to survive four or five months of such conditions providing they have stored enough branches and twigs underwater to supply them with bark to eat. Beavers provide a whole range of valuable resources for their human predators and their spread northwards as the ice retreated would have helped humans to move northwards too, especially as a source of warm fur, and late-winter fat (Coles 2010; Brown *et al.* 2017).

Recently, two beaver bones from Gough's Cave in the Mendips have been radiocarbon dated to some 12,000 years ago, by which time the climate was beginning to get colder again (Marr 2016). It seems very likely that as yet undated beaver bones from other cave systems of the broad Severn catchment, from King Arthur's and Merlin's caves at Symond's Yat on the Wye, are also of late Palaeolithic date (Coles 2006, 75-76). The confluence of the Wye and the Monnow is about five kilometres downstream of King Arthur's cave, and from shortly above the confluence the current border between England and Wales follows the Monnow for some distance. In catchment terms, which are more relevant to late Palaeolithic beaver expansion than the present humanly-defined borders, there can be little doubt that if beavers reached the Wye in the vicinity of Symond's Yat, then they were also in the Monnow. Moreover, to reach the Wye they would have spread up the Lower Severn which in the late Palaeolithic had its estuary on a coastline much further to the southwest than at present, with the Wye as one of its many tributaries. Between them, the Severn and the Wye offered a plethora of routes into Wales, and beavers would have spread as far as time and suitable habitat allowed. Following the warm centuries of the Windermere interstadial there was a cold snap, the final stage of the last glaciation, which brought the Pleistocene to an end. It lasted about 1500 years, and during this time most of the temperate fauna and flora retreated southwards once more.

For the earlier part of the current geological era, the Holocene, from about 9500 BC to about 2000 BC, the situation with regard to beavers in Wales remains similar, with as yet no direct evidence but beavers known to have been present on the other side of the Severn estuary, in the Mendips and the Somerset Levels. It is again reasonable to suggest that in Wales they colonised the Severn and Wye catchments at a minimum, and probably beyond. This suggestion is reinforced by looking at the whole of Britain in this period, with beaver remains patchy in their distribution but identified as far to the north as the Moray Firth. Given the ability of beavers to adapt to a wide range of conditions, it can be said with confidence that from an early stage in the Holocene they were as well distributed across Britain as humans. The patchy distribution of evidence is due not to local absences of beavers, but to the vagaries of history that have affected both the survival of the evidence and the opportunities for its discovery and recognition.

Later prehistory: Newton Moor and Caldicot

From about 2000 BC the situation changes, with tangible evidence from two well-recorded recent excavations. One of these sites, on Newton Moor near Cowbridge in south Wales, is best known for the silver brooch that was found there, rather than for the beaver-gnawed wood. When the brooch was discovered, in peaty ground near the river Thaw, Mark Redknap of National Museum Wales led investigations to determine whether or not the silver brooch was Treasure Trove (Redknap 1991). In the course of this work and subsequent survey by the Glamorgan-Gwent Archaeological Trust (GGAT), the area where the brooch had been found was revealed as a former landscape of pools and irregular channels interspersed with small islands, with some pieces of wood lying around in the two areas excavated. At least two of the pieces of wood showed signs of beaver gnawing (Fig 2.3). Three bits of wood were sampled for radiocarbon dating, with results indicating that two of them had grown at some time in the latter half of the second millennium BC (1500 – 1000 BC), and the third more recently, at some time in the mid-centuries of the first millennium BC (700 – 300 BC). These dates indicate that the wood grew and was then gnawed by beavers long before the brooch was made, let alone when it came to rest in the wet ground. The brooch may have been buried in a hole dug into the peaty ground, or deposited or lost in water after localised erosion had removed sediments of the intervening years. It could even have been the intervening generations of beavers that caused the erosion, for their activities do tend to create new paths and waterflows at the same time as they dam up existing ones. The channels and pools revealed during the excavation are typical of a well-developed beaver territory in a flat valley floor (Fig 2.4), and Newton Moor may have seen a series of shifting, overlapping beaver territories through the centuries indicated by the radiocarbon dates. In addition to the silver brooch, a number of later prehistoric metal artefacts have been retrieved from the Thaw valley and there may have been a tradition amongst humans here, as elsewhere in Britain, of depositing precious objects in beaver-influenced pools.

Fig. 2.3
Ffigur 2.3

a) Prehistoric wood cut
by a human using an axe.

a) Pren cynhanes wedi'i dorri
gan ddyn gan ddefnyddio bwyell.

b) Prehistoric wood
gnawed by a beaver.

b) Pren cynhanes wedi'i
gnoi gan afanc.

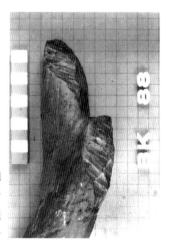

The second excavation to have produced tangible beaver evidence took place in the Nedern valley, some fifty kilometres east of Newton Moor. In the course of landscaping to enhance a country park beside Caldicot Castle, waterlogged wood and some human artefacts were found. The subsequent archaeological investigations were carried out by GGAT for Cadw, the historic environment service of the Welsh government (Nayling and Caseldine 1997). They exposed a complex series of former channels of the Nedern, and evidence for human construction in the form of probable bridge supports and other suggestions of river crossings and associated activities during the Bronze Age, approximately 2000 – 800

BC. In addition to the humanly-worked wood, several of the pieces retrieved from the sediments had been gnawed by beavers (Brunning and O'Sullivan 1997). There were five gnawed pieces from early in the Bronze Age, and twelve from late in the Bronze Age; all were young roundwood, being side branches or the stems of saplings. Hazel predominated (twelve pieces), with one piece each of hawthorn and dogwood or guelder rose. The beavers had eaten the bark from a number of the pieces, and this together with the relative slenderness of the stems suggests they were left-overs from beavers felling for food rather than for building. Quite probably there was a beaver feeding station nearby, and there may have been a dam a short distance downstream, which slowed the flow of water and led to the wood sinking into the shallow waters at the bank edge.

Fig. 2.4 A beaver in shallow water within the Bevis Trust enclosure in Carmarthenshire, among the branches of a fallen tree which has many patches of recent beaver gnawing and nibbling – a scene similar perhaps to that found at Newton Moor. *Photo Alicia Leow-Dyke, Welsh Beaver Project.*

Ffigur 2.4 Afanc mewn dŵr bas yn safle Ymddiriedolaeth Bevis yn Sir Gaerfyrddin, yng nghanol canghennau coeden sydd wedi syrthio sydd â llawer o olion afanc yn ei chnoi – sefyllfa debyg efallai i'r un a ganfuwyd ar Ros Newton. *Llun Alicia Leow-Dyke, Prosiect Afancod Cymru.*

Animal bone was relatively well preserved at Caldicot, and both small and large birds, and fish and amphibians were identified, as well as mammals. It is worth noting that the Cadw funding for the investigations made it possible to process samples by flotation and sieving, to retrieve small and fragmentary ecofacts and artefacts, and three specialist zooarchaeologists have worked on the varied assemblage of animal remains from the site (see McCormick, Hamilton-Dyer and Murphy 1997). This investment was made in part because good bone survival is relatively rare in Wales, and Caldicot was seen as an opportunity not to be missed. The results fully justified the decision, with a great variety of species identified. There was just one beaver bone, a femur from the same later Bronze Age levels as the bulk of the beaver-gnawed wood. Other wetland and aquatic species from the Bronze Age levels include water vole, frog and toad, salmon, eel, flounder and stickleback, goose, varied ducks (mallard and tufted duck, and perhaps wigeon and pintail), crane, heron and little grebe. The surrounding landscape supported cattle, horse, sheep or goats, red and roe deer, fox and field vole, and dog – and although no human bones were identified, the archaeological evidence indicates that they too were present. The picture is of a varied, partly wooded landscape, with marshes, ponds or lakes and rivers or streams, and beavers will have played an important role in creating and maintaining the varied habitat.

Fig. 2.5 Human using a beaver dam to cross a river in Brittany, as humans may have done at Caldicot.

Ffigur 2.5 Dyn yn defnyddio argae afanc i groesi afon yn Llydaw, fel y gwnaeth pobl yng Nghaldicot efallai.

It is possible that the humans were first attracted to cross the Nedern at this point because a beaver dam provided a convenient causeway (Fig. 2.5), and humans no doubt knew that the locations where beavers make their dams are usually appropriate for bridge building. The complexity of the sediments and channel features at Caldicot could be due to a succession of dams, causeways and bridges built sometimes by beavers and sometimes by humans, the former intent on ponding up the water and the latter on crossing it, while neither species wanted their structure to be swept away by the currents.

Avanke, Bever, Castor

After the main period of human activity at Caldicot, there is a further hint of beaver activity on the Nedern, in the form of probable animal burrows which were revealed during the excavations by the slightly different colour and texture of their fill. Recorded in a photograph (Nayling pers. com.) the burrows look to have been about 50cm in diameter. This is within the 30 – 80cm range for beaver burrows (Fig. 2.6), and it is unlikely that any other animal of the time would have been making burrows of this size in such a wet environment. Archaeologists are not normally on the look-out for beaver burrows, and the Caldicot example was only recognised from the photograph, some time after the excavations had been completed. There may well have been other signs of beaver activity there, and most probably many other watery and wetland contexts hold the potential for similar discoveries, once people know what to look for. The same is clearly the case with the recognition of beaver-gnawed wood, for accurate identification people need to know what it looks like. Chapter 5 discusses this point further, and it is probable that in years to come, with the general public's growing familiarity with beavers and their activities and gnawed wood, the record of the former presence of beavers in Wales will grow.

Fig. 2.6 A beaver bank-burrow entrance, revealed by the collapse of the dam immediately downstream. The probable burrow at Caldicot was of similar size.

Ffigur 2.6 Mynedfa i dwll afanc mewn glan, a ddatgelir gyda dymchweliad yr argae yn union oddi tanodd i lawr yr afon. Roedd y twll tebygol yng Nghaldicot o faint tebyg.

CHAPTER 3
EVIDENCE FROM THE MEDIEVAL PERIOD

In Wales, there is scarcely a hint of beaver presence for about 1500 years following the later Bronze Age; this is very little time compared to the long eras of prehistory, but a considerable period when seen from an historian's perspective. The paucity of evidence does not necessarily mean there were no beavers, and it is likely they did survive in Wales, as they were present in other parts of Britain. It could be that they had become relatively scarce in the time leading up to the Roman invasions, due to intensive hunting for beaver furs to export to the Romanised world. As we have already seen, when beavers come under heavy pressure from their human predators, the ones that survive are those that live out of sight of the hunters. The survivors are often those living on the wider, deeper rivers where they can hide almost literally under people's noses. They would sometimes need to come on land for food, but they are mostly nocturnal, and the chances of humans seeing a beaver would be much reduced. A hunter out on a clear moon- or star-lit night might catch a glimpse of a beaver, while people walking the river banks late on a summer's evening might have seen a beaver swimming in the distance, or heard the cracking splash of the beaver's tail slapping the water in alarm. Along the big rivers, and around the lakes of Wales too, once beavers had established a well-developed 'pasture' of bushy growth they could feed out of sight of humans, thus further ensuring their unrecorded survival. Remote valleys high in the hills and mountains, rarely visited by humans, may also have harboured some small relic populations.

There are also times when the nature of human activity and other external factors combine in a way that reduces the chance of evidence being preserved. Similarly, combinations of factors in the present day may reduce the extent of archaeological investigations in particular contexts. So it is that flood-plain development in the present day has revealed much evidence from past periods of intense human activity in these environments. A slow-down in modern development, due to economic circumstances perhaps, or to an awareness that flood-plains are not the best of places for human settlement, will reduce the rate of new discoveries. Where beavers are concerned, we have already seen the need for people to be familiar with beaver evidence for it to be recognised and recorded. Bearing these factors in mind, it is not surprising that there are periods when beaver evidence is lacking. But when the following centuries provide a strong record of beaver presence, this suggests they were there all along. This is the case for Wales, where beavers are well documented in the medieval period. It is the advent of literacy and the passing on of knowledge through the written record than brings beavers back into the picture, in one case through legislation concerning the value of animal skins.

The Laws of Hywel Dda

Hywel Dda, Howell the Good, was a powerful king whose authority stretched over much of Wales by the time of his death in 950 AD. He is remembered as the founder of Welsh law, brought together as the Laws of Hywel Dda. There is no surviving version of the Laws from his reign, but copies were made, and copied in their turn, and today the earliest surviving examples come from the 13th century. Daniel Huws, commenting on one of the earliest extant copies known as manuscript Peniarth 28, suggests that the later copies retain a core of late 1st millennium AD laws, as well as material added later (Huws 1989). It is not entirely clear when the section relevant to beavers became incorporated, probably later than the reign of Hywel Dda, but no later than the 13th century. A number of the Laws relate to the value given to diverse elements of the natural world, including animal skins. Those of deer and cattle were valued at twelve pence each, as were the skins of otters (*Lutra lutra*) and stoats (*Mustela erminae*). Marten (*Martes martes,* pine marten) were valued at twenty-four pence, and beavers at 120 pence. The Laws in addition stated that 'the King is to have the worth of Beavers, Martens and Ermines in whatsoever spot they are killed, because from them, the borders of the King's garments are made'. In the Laws, the name used for beavers was *Llostlydan*, meaning Broad-tail, and qualified as *befyr* or beaver.

A number of people have commented with some surprise on the high value of a beaver pelt compared to the other species. To take one influential example, Barrett-Hamilton and Hinton (1921) suggested that beavers must have been 'extremely scarce' when the price was set, since their pelt was worth so much compared to other species. I think that a furrier would take a different view of the values, surprised perhaps at the low value of twelve pence set for stoats, which in their white winter coats provide the much sought-after ermine, and finding the qualities of the dense, warm, waterproof pelt of the beaver properly appreciated in its valuation at 120 pence. Dent (1974, 54-55) makes this point slightly facetiously, pointing out that for many centuries the only alternative waterproof head gear to a beaver hat was sticky tarred cloth or smelly oilskin.

It could be that the difference in the values was simply based on size. The average adult beaver (120 pence) weighs twenty kilos or more, an adult marten (twenty-four pence) about two kilos and a stoat/ermine (twelve pence) about 500g. The pelt from a beaver body would cover about the same area as five or six marten pelts, or ten to twelve ermine (Fig. 3.1), and this is perhaps what is reflected in the 120 pence to twenty-four pence to twelve pence valuations: one chunky beaver body is six times bigger than a marten and ten time bigger than a long slender stoat. Seen in this light, the Laws suggest a group of high-value luxury skins consisting of beaver, marten, ermine and probably otter, and a group of less valuable skins which included deer and cattle despite their size. Beavers may or may not have been scarce, but they yielded ten times the area of luxury fur as a stoat and their pelt was worth ten times as much.

The prestige accorded to beaver, marten and ermine skins, evident in their use for the King's garments, continued for many centuries, and was no doubt another factor affecting the valuations. Veale provides a nice story to illustrate how furs from different species were perceived:

> One of the luxuries solemnly cast aside by medieval ascetics was the wearing of furs of marten, goatskin being preferred. Perhaps the clearest statement of contemporary views emerges from a story told about the Saxon Wulfstan, the eleventh-century Bishop of Worcester, whose admirers pointed out to him that even if he did not wear sable, beaver, or fox as he ought to, he might at least wear catskins rather than lambskins. 'Believe me,' retorted the Bishop, 'men sing oftener of the Lamb of God than of the cat of God.' (Veale 1966, 4)

Taking these various points together, it can be argued that when the section on beavers was incorporated into the Laws, beavers were highly prized in Wales, and not necessarily scarce. The high value of their skin would have been an incentive to hunt the beavers, but we know that they were not driven to extinction.

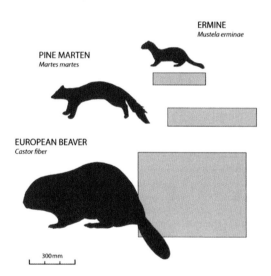

Fig. 3.1 a) Beavers are substantially bigger than Pine Marten and Ermine, and their pelts provide a larger area of fur.

Ffigur 3.1 a) Mae afancod yn sylweddol fwy na Bele'r Coed a Charlwm, ac mae eu crwyn yn darparu arwynebedd mwy o ffwr.

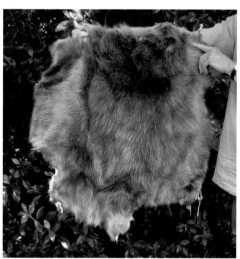

Fig. 3.1 b) the size of a beaver pelt in relation to a human.

Ffigur 3.1 b) maint croen afanc mewn perthynas â dyn.

Gerald of Wales - Giraldus Cambrensis

Gerald of Wales, a man renowned for his descriptive accounts of Wales and Ireland, is the person who tells us that beavers were still to be found in Wales. Towards the end of the 12th century AD, he described the habits of beavers in general, and wrote specifically about those living on Afon Teifi in south-west Wales. His writings have since become one of the keys to our understanding of beavers in Britain in the Middle Ages. The beaver passages occur in the *Itinerary through Wales* (IW) and the *Description of Wales* (DW), and in the *History and Topography of Ireland* (HTI) (Hoare 1806; O'Meara 1982; Thorpe 1978). There has been some debate about the accuracy of his observations, but I have argued elsewhere for the reliability of much of what he wrote on the subject (Coles 2006, 166 – 170). He was not, however, infallible, and the current beginnings of recovery for the European beaver populations, which have enabled modern studies of their behaviour, indicates that while Gerald got more right than some later commentators thought, he also got some things wrong.

Gerald was born in south-west Wales, to a family of mixed Norman and Welsh heritage; his education was to take him from St David's to Gloucester and then to Paris, and he visited Rome several times. Thus, he probably grew up within reach of the Teifi, and knew about the beavers there as a child. He may well have encountered more beavers on the Severn and its tributaries when he was in Gloucester, and along the Seine in Paris in his later student and teaching days. Both Seine and Severn have a number of beaver associations, for example the river Bièvre which joins the Seine in Paris, and the cluster of beaver place-names on the Severn in and around Worcester. Later, Gerald spent a year in Ireland, in 1183, and he returned there with Prince John in 1185. He had a strong and well-informed interest in natural history, and while he was in Ireland he established that the island lacked several of the species of animal native to Britain, including beavers. In 1188, having already written his account of Ireland, he travelled with the Archbishop of Canterbury through Wales to raise support for the Third Crusade, and the *Itinerary* and *Description* were written as a result.

The *Itinerary through Wales*, which I will use here, has the longest of Gerald's accounts of beavers. The English version quoted below is from Richard Colt Hoare's 1806 translation from the original Latin, edited by Llewelyn Williams (1908, 106 - 109). Where a more recent translation by Lewis Thorpe (1978) makes an obscure passage clearer, or adds useful detail that Hoare omitted, I have added the words from Thorpe in square brackets. Following each section of Gerald's text, I have made an evaluation of each of the main points, based for the most part on my direct observation of beavers and their territories during the Beaver Works Project and other European field visits. In the *Itinerary*, the beaver passage comes in Book II, Chapter III, 'Of the River Teivi, Cardigan and Emelyn', which opens with a description of the abundant salmon in the river, and the way they leap the waterfall near Cilgerran, and then turns to the beavers living on the river (Fig. 3.2):

> *The Teivi has another singular particularity, being the only river in Wales, or even in England, which has beavers; in Scotland they are said to be found in one river, but are very scarce.*

Fig. 3.2 Afon Teifi at Cilgerran. In the late 12th century Gerald of Wales wrote that both salmon and beavers could be found here.

Ffigur 3.2 Afon Teifi yng Nghilgerran. Tua diwedd y 12fed ganrif ysgrifennodd Gerallt Gymro bod eogiaid ac afancod i'w gweld yma.

Before writing the *Itinerary*, Gerald had already made this point about the Teifi; in HTI (part I, section 20) he wrote 'Ireland has badgers but not beavers. In Wales beavers are found only in the Teifi river near Cardigan. They are, in the same way, scarce in Scotland.' This passage introduces the beaver as a river-dwelling animal, it suggests Gerald knew of the Teifi beavers before he set off on his Welsh journey, and it shows that he had been enquiring about the distribution of beavers in general terms. Their presence in Scotland is confirmed by later sources, and beavers are thought to have survived in that country at least until the early 16th century (see Coles 2006). However, Gerald was wrong in respect of England. We know this thanks to a recent discovery from Scaup Burn in Northumberland, close to the Scottish border. Here, in 2011, a group of ecologists retrieved several pieces of wood sticking out from the exposed bank of the burn, about one metre below ground level. One of the pieces of wood had been cut by humans, and one had been gnawed by beavers, both in the later 14th century AD (Manning *et al.* 2014), several generations after Gerald made his observations. The significance of this discovery for the later history of beavers in Wales is explored further in Chapter 6.

> I think it not a useless labour, to insert a few remarks respecting the nature of these animals; the manner in which they bring their materials from the woods to the water, and with what skill they connect them in the construction of their dwellings in the midst of rivers; their means of defence on the eastern and western sides against hunters [how they protect their dwellings in western countries and in the east against those who hunt them]; and also concerning their fish-like tails [rather than what one would expect in a land animal].

This introduction makes clear that Gerald's account of beavers is to be a general one, not restricted to the Teifi inhabitants.

Fig. 3.3 Beavers usually transport twigs and branches by holding them in their mouth (there is a convenient gap between the incisors and cheek teeth) and towing them through the water. *Photo Alicia Leow-Dyke, Welsh Beaver Project.*

Ffigur 3.3 Fel arfer mae afancod yn cludo brigau a changhennau drwy eu dal yn eu ceg (mae bylchau hwylus rhwng y blaenddannedd a dannedd y foch) a'u llusgo drwy'r dŵr. *Llun Alicia Leow-Dyke, Prosiect Afancod Cymru.*

The beavers, in order to construct their castles in the middle of rivers, make use of the animals of their own species instead of carts, who, by a wonderful mode of carriage, convey the timber from the woods to the rivers. Some of them, obeying the dictates of nature, receive on their bellies the logs of wood cut off by their associates, which they hold tight with their feet, and thus with transverse pieces placed in their mouths, are drawn along backwards, with their cargo, by other beavers, who fasten themselves with their teeth to the raft. The moles [badgers] use a similar artifice in clearing out the dirt from the cavities they form by scraping.

Beavers do not transport wood in the way described here. They gnaw at wood growing close to the water's edge to detach manageable lengths, usually no more than three metres long, and then they trim off any awkward side-branches. They carry one piece at a time, held in their mouth by the fat end and towed through the water (Fig. 3.3). To take a piece of wood overland, the beavers similarly first gnaw it to a manageable length, and then grasp it between their teeth and drag it down to the water's edge, from where they can tow it to where it is needed, dam or lodge or underwater foodstore. Beavers are most active from dusk to dawn, and it is possible that Gerald never saw for himself how they move lengths of wood.

Fig. 3.4 A beaver lodge in south-east France, in a setting such as Gerald envisaged.

Ffigur 3.4 Gwâl afancod yn ne ddwyrain Ffrainc, mewn lleoliad fel y rhagwelodd Gerallt.

Beaver lodge cut open to show interior. The lower part is the drying and dining floor ; the raised part is the bed. Dimensions (inside), 4 feet 10 inches long, 4 feet 5 inches wide, 2 feet 1 inch high ; lower floor, 4 inches above water ; bed floor, 6 inches higher.

Fig. 3.5 An early 20th century photo of a beaver lodge, in Canada, cut away to show the lower and upper platforms within, and a glimpse of the water-filled access burrow to the lower right. *Radclyffe-Dugmore 1914.*

Ffigur 3.5 Llun o ddechrau'r ugeinfed ganrif o wâl afancod yng Nghanada, wedi'i dorri i ffwrdd i ddangos y llwyfannau isaf ac uchaf tu mewn, a chipolwg ar y twll mynediad llawn dŵr yn y gwaelod ar y dde. *Radclyffe-Dugmore 1914.*

In some deep and still corner of the river, the beavers use such skill in the construction of their habitations, that not a drop of water can penetrate, or the force of storms shake them; nor do they fear any violence but that of mankind, nor even that, unless well armed. They entwine the branches of willows with other wood, and different kinds of leaves, to the usual height of the water, and having made within-side a communication from floor to floor, they elevate a kind of stage, or scaffold, from which they may observe and watch the rising of the waters.

Beavers select deep water to cover and protect the underwater entrance to their den, and, as noted in Chapter 1, if the water is not deep enough they will build a dam to raise the level; this usually happens on streams rather than rivers. The water is likely to be still, because of the dam, or at least slow-flowing if naturally deep. Above-ground lodges or 'habitations' are usually very solid, water-tight structures which withstand attack from most predators if well maintained, and the only way in or out is along a water-filled burrow (Fig. 3.4). Willow and other wood and leafy twigs, uprooted plants and mud and stones are used in the building. Inside the heap of materials, there will be a feeding platform just above water-level, and a sleeping platform a bit higher up (Fig. 3.5; see also Fig. 1.8). Over time and in places where there are marked seasonal variations in water-level, a lodge may spread and rise to have feeding and sleeping platforms at higher levels, as well as the lower ones (Kitchener 2001). Gerald's account of a beaver lodge is therefore based on accurate observation. However, although they do like to sit at dawn on a sloping bank or other high spot, where they can catch the rising sun and groom themselves before retiring to their den to sleep, beavers are not known to make a raised place where they can keep a watch for rising waters. Within their den, they can monitor rising water levels just by looking at the plunge-hole.

In the course of time, their habitations bear the appearance of a grove of willow trees, rude and natural without, but artfully constructed within.

Fig. 3.6 A well-established lodge amongst willows and other trees, on the bank of the river Ellez in Brittany.

Ffigur 3.6 Gwâl wedi sefydlu'n dda yng nghanol helyg a choed eraill ar lan afon Ellez yn Llydaw.

Fresh green wood plunged into organic-rich mud will often take root, particularly if it is willow. Many well-established beaver lodges look from the outside very much as Gerald describes, as the rooted willow branches grow into a sheltering clump (Fig. 3.6). To see within a den, only a child-sized human could wriggle up the burrow, but abandoned lodges tend to develop a hole in the top, through which a human observer could see the hollowed-out den with sleeping and feeding platforms and one or more plunge-holes (burrows) leading from the lowest platform into the water.

> *This animal can remain in or under water at its pleasure, like the frog or seal, who shew, by the smoothness or roughness of their skins, the flux and reflux of the sea. These three animals, therefore, live indifferently under the water, or in the air, and have short legs, broad bodies, stubbed tails, and resemble the mole in their corporal shape [they are made rather in the shape of moles or badgers].*

Fig. 3.7 A beaver in the Llangors enclosure, about to slip into the water, and giving a good view of its broad, flat and hairless tail. *Photo Alicia Leow-Dyke, Welsh Beaver Project.*

Ffigur 3.7 Afanc ar safle Llangors, ar fin llithro i'r dŵr, ac yn dangos ei gynffon lydan, wastad heb flew yn glir. *Llun Alicia Leow-Dyke, Prosiect Afancod Cymru.*

Beavers can stay under water for about fifteen minutes at a time if they do not exert themselves, or four to five minutes if swimming (Kitchener 2001, 29); they can swim quite fast, up to two metres per second, and have been known to swim up to 800m underwater in one dive. If they swim through their underwater burrows up to their dens they can take breath without any land-based observer seeing them. Potentially, therefore, a beaver could work its way rapidly from one end of a 1500m territory to the other without emerging into the open at all. Gerald's comment that a beaver can remain underwater 'at its pleasure', while not entirely accurate, conveys well how a human might have understood a beaver's long disappearance under water. As for tails, the beaver's is broad and flat, and one might call it stubby in the sense of 'blunt' (Fig. 3.7). In other respects the comparison with frogs, seals, badgers and moles is reasonable, and interesting in showing how Gerald was observing and thinking about the causes of similarities between animals, frogs and seals in water, badgers and moles on land.

> *It is worthy of remark, that the beaver has but four teeth, two above, and two below, which being broad and sharp, cut like a carpenter's axe, and as such he uses them.*

As noted in Chapter 2, beavers have four large incisors, which would be easily seen by a human. The incisors are long and sharp, and used to cut wood. They leave very distinctive marks which archaeologists, myself included, have sometimes mistaken for the facets left by humans using stone or metal blades (see Figs 1.7 and 2.3). A beaver's cheek teeth are smaller and much less visible than the incisors, which might account for Gerald's misunderstanding in this respect. Over a period of several days or weeks, and sometimes even years, beavers will fell quite large trees, using their teeth to tear away long chips of wood from all sides of the trunk, until the tree falls (Fig. 3.8).

Fig. 3.8 Beavers felling a tree turn their heads at right angles to the trunk to bite into the wood, using their upper incisors to anchor the bite and their lower incisors to cut into the wood. *Photo Lars Wilsson 1964.*

Ffigur 3.8 Afancod yn torri coeden ac yn troi eu pennau ar ongl sgwâr i'r boncyff i frathu i mewn i'r pren gan ddefnyddio eu blaenddannedd uchaf i angori'r brathiad a'u blaenddannedd isaf i dorri i mewn i'r pren. *Llun Lars Wilsson 1964.*

They make excavations and dry hiding places in the banks near their dwelling,

Within their territory, a beaver family may have a number of burrows leading to subsidiary dens in the bank, as well as one or more visible above-ground lodges. Conditions in some territories allow for numerous bank-dens and no above-ground structures are needed. The subsidiary dens are used by all members of a beaver family to rest up during periods of activity, or as a secure retreat from predators, and they are likely to be used by the male and the sub-adults of a family when the adult female takes over the main den to give birth to her next litter.

> *and when they hear the stroke of the hunter, who with sharp poles endeavours to penetrate them, they fly as soon as possible to the defence of their castle, having first blown out the water from the entrance of the hole, and rendered it foul and muddy by scraping the earth, in order thus artfully to elude the stratagems of the well-armed hunter, who is watching them from the opposite banks of the river[holding his metal three-pronged spear and waiting for the beaver to spring out].*

The recent history of beavers in Europe, their near-extinction and gradual recovery thanks to legal protection of the species, has given little opportunity to see how they react when hunted by humans. Where they are prolific in Europe, they are in some countries hunted under licence, usually by shooting which relies on surprising them in the open. In North America beavers have for long been trapped, often underwater, again a method that relies on getting the beaver before it becomes aware of the danger. In this instance, therefore, present-day human and beaver behaviour is little guide to the accuracy or otherwise of Gerald's observation. I have sometimes wondered if the phrase 'to muddy the waters' stems from beaver habits, but cannot trace its origin.

> *When the beaver finds he cannot save himself from the pursuit of the dogs who follow him, that he may ransom his body by the sacrifice of a part, he throws away that, which by natural instinct he knows to be the object sought for, and in the sight of the hunter castrates himself, from which circumstance he has gained the name of Castor; and if by chance the dogs should chase an animal which had been previously castrated, he has the sagacity to run to an elevated spot, and there lifting up his leg, shews the hunter that the object of his pursuit is gone. Cicero speaking of them says, "They ransom themselves by that part of the body, for which they are chiefly sought." And Juvenal says, "....Qui se eunuchum ipse facit, cupiens evadere damno testiculi" . ["This beast himself a eunuch makes, but saves his life at least without his testicles"] And St Bernard "Prodit enim castor proprio de corpore velox reddere quas hostis avarus opes." ["The beaver saves his life by offering at full speed those vital organs which the lustful hunters need"].*

This story of the beaver's self-castration is at least as old as Aesop's *Fables* of the mid-6th century BC, and was repeated by many, including the authors of medieval Bestiaries or collections of moral tales based on animals. The surviving manuscript Bestiaries often have illustrations, and for the beaver tale the depiction usually includes a hunter, dogs and a beaver in the act of biting off his testicles. However old and venerable the story, it is in fact a well and truly garbled version of reality. Humans did hunt beavers for more than their fur, and they did make some use of beaver testicles. But the main prize alongside fur consisted of the castoreum glands, highly sought after as medicine (Fig. 3.9). Both male and female beavers have two castoreum glands internally, close to their anal glands (Coles 2006, fig. 11.8). Both sets of glands appear to be used by the beavers for territorial marking and for communication with each other, especially with individuals outside their own family – beavers are highly territorial, and fight off any intruding beavers, so they need some means of communicating their status without a direct encounter. The castoreum glands of a live beaver would not be visible in any way, which may have prompted the development of the castration story. To add to the confusion, male beavers do not have external, visible testicles but internal ones, alongside the anal and castoreum glands. Thus humans might think no beavers had testicles, because they had never seen them, yet they knew castoreum came from beavers and people hunted the beavers to obtain it, and a story evolved to fit the apparent facts.

Fig. 3.9 A bundle of castoreum sacs hung up to dry. Taken in North America, the photo shows castoreum sacs from *Castor Canadensis*.

Ffigur 3.9 Pentwr o godenni castorewm wedi'u hongian i sychu. Wedi'i dynnu yng Ngogledd America, mae'r llun yn dangos codenni castorewm *Castor Canadensis*.

Later, the story was adapted as a Christian morality tale. Charles Wilson, in the mid-19th century, discussed the original fable, and pointed out that Pliny in *Naturalis Historia* (c. AD 77/79) had corrected Aesop's misinterpretation, but this did nothing to prevent the continuing popularity of the self-castration myth (Wilson 1858). Humans, it seems, have long had a penchant for using animals to tell stories, without worrying too much about the accuracy of their facts, and Gerald was happy to repeat the beaver tale with its added Christian moral.

Thus, therefore, in order to preserve his skin, which is sought after in the west,
and the medicinal part of his body, which is coveted in the east, although
he cannot save himself entirely, yet, by a wonderful instinct and sagacity, he
endeavours to avoid the stratagems of his pursuers.

By the later Middle Ages, we have good documentary evidence for the trade in beaver skins (Veale 2003), which were being imported to Britain from many sources, from Portugal to northern Eurasia and later from North America. The skins were certainly sought after by western Europeans, though not exclusively by them. Castoreum was held to vary according to region, and indeed probably did vary in its composition according to the beavers' local diet. Gerald would have been familiar with a number of the comments on castoreum from classical sources, including that of Strabo (c.63 BC- AD 24) who held that castoreum from Spain was inferior to that from Pontus, in what is now northern Turkey close to the Black Sea. The medicinal value of castoreum was set out by Celsus in *De Medicina* (c. AD 30), and many people clearly set high store by it. Thus, castoreum was coveted in the east, but used in the west too, and the trade has continued to the present-day. Gerald's association of castoreum with the east and skins with the west is not wrong, but neither is it the whole truth: both were exploited across Eurasia.

The beavers have broad, short tails, thick, like the palm of a hand, which they
use as a rudder in swimming;

A beaver's tail is broad and flat, but not unusually short (see Fig. 3.7); compared to a stoat or pine-marten, both of which have tails that are usually at least half the length of their head-plus-body, the beaver's tail is usually about a third the length of its head-plus-body (based on measurements from Macdonald and Barrett 1993). The comparison with the palm of a hand is apt in terms of thickness. As for swimming, the beaver's tail is very important, used both as a rudder and for propulsion.

and although the rest of their body is hairy, this part, like that of seals, is
without hair, and smooth; upon which account, in Germany and the arctic
regions, where beavers abound, great and religious persons, in times of fasting,
eat the tails of this fish-like animal, as having both the taste and colour of fish.

A beaver tail looks hairless and scaly, although under magnification residual hairs are visible between the scales (Kitchener 2001, 18). In the autumn, beavers build up fat reserves in their tail, which are important to their survival through the late winter. Humans have long hunted beavers to eat as well as for their skins and castoreum, and still do so, and in the second millennium AD the practice of eating beavers was more widespread than suggested by Gerald. There is evidence that beaver-tail was regarded as fish, and thought suitable for a Lenten dish in a great household, from John Russell's *Boke of Nurture* written in the mid-15th century (Russell, ed. Furnivall 1868, 153-155). In England, beaver bones have been found at three high-status medieval sites, Castle Acre in Norfolk, the Old Bishop's Palace in Winchester, and Jarrow on the outskirts of Newcastle upon Tyne. These sites are associated with 'great and religious persons' and the beaver bones come from contexts that are not very precisely dated but probably contemporary with Gerald or later, and probably represent food debris. Gerald, however, implies a certain personal doubt about the fishy character of beavers.

To summarise, Gerald's account of beavers and their activities is accurate in parts, weak in others, and occasionally wrong. With regard to their supposed habit of self-castration, he was following a well-known but inaccurate story that had persisted for centuries despite Pliny's attempt at correction, and his description of how beavers transport wood was equally misguided. He was partially wrong with regard to their teeth, in missing the cheek teeth, but right about the prominence of the incisors. His description of the outward appearance of a beaver was reasonably accurate, as were his comments on their use of tail as rudder, and beavers do stay under water for long periods, though not indefinitely. He was correct that beavers dig bank-dens as well as building lodges, and correct in his account of different 'floors' within a lodge, and he provides a good description of how a lodge is built and how it comes over time to look like a willow-grove. In terms of human exploitation of beavers, for fur and castoreum and to eat, what he writes is on the whole accurate, but incomplete in some respects. It would seem that Gerald knew his classical sources well with regard to beavers, and that he was familiar with the main features of active beaver territories, and had seen beavers swimming. He may have talked to beaver-hunters, and seen a dead beaver but not dissected one. In the context of his time, he was well informed, and most accurate for those aspects where he had probably had the opportunity for direct observation, in the catchments of the Severn and the Seine, and closer to home along the Teifi. It would be unfair to chide him for not knowing of the beavers in Northumberland, in the remote uplands of the Wharfe catchment, since the evidence of their late presence there was only discovered very recently. For several centuries following his important work, there is no known account from Britain to match the description of beavers given by Gerald of Wales.

CHAPTER 4

AN AWARENESS OF BEAVERS IN WALES,
FROM THE TUDORS TO THE VICTORIAN ERA

From the early 16th century to the late 19th century, the bulk of the evidence for beavers in Wales again comes from the records made by humans. There are changes in the way knowledge was spread and in the means of access to learning, reflecting changes in the human world, such as the development of printing. In Wales, as in England, there was a notable expansion of scholarship, following the Renaissance and perhaps aided by the establishment of the Tudor monarchy and by the Reformation. Although beavers were rarely of paramount significance, both trends contributed to a wider awareness of their former presence in the native fauna. The gradual expansion of knowledge and changing ideas can be traced through the work of successive scholars, both Welsh and English, who touched upon the subject of beavers in their writings. Searching for references to beavers has incidentally revealed some of the vagaries and inconsistencies of the published record, a reminder not to believe everything that is printed. It has also shown the enthusiasm, scope and dedication of many scholars, and the networks of communication that were established, long before the Penny Post, let alone the internet.

This chapter explores the background of scholars interested in beavers, and assesses their awareness of the species. There is a long-established general assumption that beavers were extinct by the late Middle Ages, and that the majority of scholars confirmed this in their writings, as revealed for example by Richard Colt Hoare's comments accompanying his translation of Gerald of Wales' writings. However, there are hints of their presence, and I have tried to take a different approach, examining the texts with the thought that beavers may have survived in some localities long after they became extinct in others. After all, this is what happened in mainland Europe.

By the Victorian era, there are no longer suggestions of beavers living wild in Britain, instead re-introductions begin. As we shall see at the end of this chapter, Wales and Scotland together retain evidence of one of the earliest and most magnificent projects for the restoration of beavers to the island of Britain.

Humphrey Llwyd (1527-1568) and *The Description of Wales*

Following Gerald's late 12th century discussion of beavers, the next known mention of their presence in Wales comes from the 16th century. It occurs in *The Description of Wales*, a work with a complex history. Until recently, it was thought to have been first written in Latin by Sir John Prise in the earlier 16th century, then translated and expanded by Humphrey Llwyd a few decades later, and finally edited and published in 1584 by David Powel as part of his *History of Cambria, now called Wales*. However, recent research by Ieuan Williams (2002) suggests that Humphrey Llwyd was the original author of the work that concerns us here, and that he completed his text by 1559, well before the 1584 publication. Llwyd (Fig. 4.1) came from Denbigh in North Wales (see frontispiece map); he was an Oxford student, and then worked for the Earl of Arundel. From about 1553 his duties took him to London and counties south of the Thames. He did not lose touch with North Wales, however, and was MP for the Denbigh boroughs from 1563-67. He died in 1568. His text, known as *Cronica Walliae,* was written in English.

Fig. 4.1 Portrait of Humphrey Llwyd, when he was in his mid-30s. *Photo ©Lyfrgell Genedlaethol Cymru - National Library of Wales.*

Ffigur 4.1 Portread o Humphrey Llwyd, yn ei dridegau. *Llun © Llyfrgell Genedlaethol Cymru.*

Llwyd began with a short introductory description of Wales, followed by an account of its history from the departure of the Romans to the later 13th century. When he was working for the Earl, he had been one of those who built up Arundel's Nonsuch library, and in doing this he would have come across a number of works relevant to his own researches, including the writings of Gerald of Wales. Llwyd's comments on beavers in *Cronica Walliae* occur in the introductory description, where he describes the rivers of South Wales. It is quoted here from Ieuan William's 2002 edition, which is based on manuscript copies of Llwyd's text, without any of the additions or alterations made by Powel for the 1584 printed edition.

> *In Tivi above all the ryvers in Wales were in Giraldus tyme a great numbre of castors, which maye be Englished bevers, and are called in Welshe avanke, which name onelye remayneth in Wales at this day, [23] but what hit meaneth very fewe can tell. Hit is a beast not muche unlike an otter but that hit is bigger, all heary savinge the tayle, which is like a fishe tayle as broade as a mans hand.*

This beast useth aswell the water as the lande and hath very sharpe teethe and bytethe cruelly till he perseave the bones cracke. His stones be of great efficacie in phisick. He that will lerne what stronge nestes, which Giraldus calleth castelles, they builde upon the face of the water with greate bowes which they cute with ther teethe and howe some lye upon ther backs holding the woode with ther foure feete which the other drawe by a crosse sticke, the which he holdeth in this mouth to the watter side, and other particularities of ther nature, let him reade Giraldus in his Topographie of Wales.

(*Cronica Walliae*, ed. Ieuan Williams 2002 p. 81)

The passage is interesting for several reasons. *Avanke* is unambiguously stated to be the Welsh name for the animal called *Castor* in Latin and *Bever* in English, by an author who was used to working in all three languages. Llwyd, as noted above, was familiar with Gerald of Wales' text on beavers, but he did not use all of it in what he wrote of beavers. Indeed, he may have been sceptical of Gerald's account of how beavers transport wood, given his almost dismissive suggestion that anyone interested can read it for themselves. But where would readers find Gerald's works at this time? David Powel was shortly to publish somewhat abridged versions of the *Itinerary* and the *Description*, but not until 1585, the year following his publication of *Cronica Walliae* as part of the *History of Cambria*.

I have argued elsewhere (Coles 2006, 180) that the first sentence of Llwyd's passage on beavers should not necessarily be interpreted as meaning that beavers were extinct in Wales, although they must have been scarce or hidden if few knew the animal. Rather, it could imply that two of the three names for the animal had fallen out of use, and the animal was currently known only as 'avanke'. Llwyd mentions two bits of information about beavers which do not come from Gerald, the cruel bite till bones crack and the comparison with an otter, both of which read as if written by someone who knew about beavers and otters, or had access to someone with first-hand knowledge of them. Both are accurate; beavers are like otters in being semi-aquatic mammals, but beavers are bigger and hairier, and when fighting between themselves or against predators they bite very deep, and cause death, not through loss of blood but from the festering of the internal wounds.

In addition to *Cronica Walliae*, Humphrey Llwyd produced the first printed Map of Wales. On a tour in Europe with the Earl of Arundel in 1566-67 he met with the Antwerp map-maker Ortelius, and on his return to Britain Llwyd was asked to make a map of Wales. This was soon done, for it was completed before his death in 1568; the map was published in 1573 by Ortelius, in the *Additamentum* to his 1570 *Theatrum Orbis Terrarum*. On the map, beside the Teifi upstream of Kilgerran, was written '*hic fluvius solus in Britannia castores habet*'- the only river in Britain to have beavers. Comments such as this were to influence later scholars, who claimed that beavers had become extinct during the Middle Ages.

A trio of English scholars

In later Tudor and Stuart times, the volume of printed works increased, as did the volume of correspondence between scholars. In the same period, the founding of the Royal Society and the development of museums all contributed to the expansion of national and international networks of scholarship. It was in this context that three English scholars touched on the presence of beavers, in Wales and elsewhere. In the writings of the Tudor period onwards, 'England and Wales' was often shortened to 'England', particularly by the English and probably to the annoyance of the Welsh, while 'Britannia' became a popular term covering the islands of Britain and Ireland.

William Harrison (1534 – 1593). William Harrison, a clergyman, historian and topographer based in south-east England, and a few years younger than Humphrey Llwyd, was another who referred to the Teifi beavers. His *Description of England* was published in 1577 as part of an extensive introductory volume to Holinshed's *Chronicles of England, Scotland and Ireland*; a second edition appeared in 1586 (Parry 2004).

In Harrison's *Description* there is a survey of the animals to be found in the island, which included a section on 'savage beasts and vermines'. The control of vermin was one of the many concerns of government at the time. Roger Lovegrove in *Silent Fields* (2007) has set out the development of legislation and local government action concerning the classification and control of wildlife regarded as vermin in England and Wales. Seen from today, the story is horrific in terms of the slaughter of animals involved. In 1566, Elizabeth I had passed *An Acte for the Preservation of Grayne*, which expanded on Henry VIII's 1532 *Acte made and ordered to dystroye Choughs, Crowes and Rokes*. The new Act, which was reviewed in 1572 and 1598, had a long list of the species regarded as vermin, extending well beyond the corvids and other grain-eaters. Bounty was to be paid on the heads of vermin, by designated churchwardens, for example two pence for an otter or a hedgehog.

In his description of the fauna of Britain, Harrison followed a paragraph on foxes and badgers with a passage on other animals classified by the new law as vermin. A number of his comments on the beuer, or beaver, suggest he had access to information in addition to that provided by Gerald of Wales:

> *'I might here intreat largelie of other vermine, as the polcat, the miniuer, the weasell, stote, fulmart, squirrill, fitchew, and such like, which Cardan includeth vnder the word Mustela: also of the otter, and likewise of the beuer, whose hinder feet and taile onlie are supposed to be fish. Certes the taile of this beast is like vnto a thin whetstone, as the bodie vnto a monsterous rat: the beast also it selfe is of such force in the teeth, that it will gnaw an hole through a thicke*

planke, or shere thorough a dubble billet in a night; it loueth also the stillest riuers: & it is given to them by nature, to go by flockes vnto the woods at hand, where they gather sticks wherewith to build their nests, wherein their bodies lie drie aboue the water, although they so prouide most commonlie, that their tailes may hang within the same. It is also reported that their said tailes are a delicate dish, and their stones of such medicinable force, that (as Vertomannus saith) foure men smelling vnto them each after other did bleed at the nose through their attractive force, proceeding from a vehement sauour wherewith they are indued: there is greatest plentie of them in Persia, cheefelie about Balascham, from whence they and their dried cods are brought into all quarters of the world, though not without some forgerie by such as provide them. And of all these here remembred, as the first sorts are plentifull in euerie wood and hedgerow: so the latter, especiallie the otter (for to saie the truth we haue not manie beuers, but only in the Teifi in Wales) is not wanting or to seek in manie, but most streams and riuers of this Ile: but it shall suffice in this sort to haue named them as I doo finallie the marterne, a beast of the chase, although for number I worthilie doubt whether that of our beuers or marterns may be thought to be the lesse.'

Harrison 1586 (reprinted 1807, 379)

Fig. 4.2 A 'dubble billet' sized beaver-gnawed tree-trunk, in south-eastern France. Beavers may gnaw at a trunk for several nights, for twenty or so minutes at a time, before the tree falls.

Ffigur 4.2 Boncyff coeden mawr wedi'i gnoi gan afanc yn ne ddwyrain Ffrainc. Bydd afancod yn cnoi boncyff am sawl noson, am ryw ugain munud ar y tro, cyn i'r goeden syrthio.

In this account, beavers follow otters, as with Humphrey Llwyd's text which was written before Harrison's but published later. Perhaps both used the same source, or both simply reflected the general assumptions of their day. Harrison's classification of both species as vermin is an interesting development, due to the new legislation and hinting at changing human attitudes to wildlife (see Lovegrove 2007 for further discussion of this point). His physical description includes a vivid picture of the beaver`s tail, and the comparison with a whetstone, rather than Gerald and Llwyd's palm of a human hand, suggests he may have had a different source, or himself seen a beaver (or maybe the shape of whetstones had changed, becoming more like a beaver's tail in outline). Like Llwyd, Harrison was impressed by the strength of a beaver's bite, and the way he illustrates it, the beaver biting though a thick plank or a double billet (a stout pole) in a night, hints at a beaver gnawing its way out of captivity. Beavers can indeed gnaw through large trunks and poles, but it usually takes them some while (Fig. 4.2).

These differences suggest that in addition to making use of Gerald's text, Harrison had drawn on other sources, possibly also known to Llwyd; Harrison's own ambit seems to have been mainly along the lower Thames from Oxford via London to Essex, and to Cambridge, all good places for beavers in former times but probably no longer so in his own day, so possibly he gained his knowledge through correspondence with or talking to people who knew about beavers and beaver trapping elsewhere in Britain or abroad.

The passage on still rivers, transport of wood, and nests (dens) is close to Gerald's account. Beaver tail, however, is for Harrison no longer the rich man's variation on fish during the dull days of fasting, as suggested for England by John Russell in the previous century, but merely a 'delicate dish'; the change in perception was a minor effect of the Reformation perhaps. The commentary on beaver stones (not in fact testicles, but castoreum sacs, as discussed above) is most probably all from the acknowledged source, Vertomannus, who was also known as Ludovico di Varthema (1470 – 1517). Vertomannus was a native of Bologna, a traveller and writer who ranged from Egypt to Borneo and beyond; he had been to Persia, where he could have observed the trade in castoreum at first hand, while his more distant travels were made in the company of a Persian merchant who may have provided further details, some of them apparently more sales talk than strictly factual.

In the final section, Harrison's interpolation about the Teifi is somewhat ambiguous but can be read as follows: all vermin are common, including the otter; beavers are 'not many' being found only on the Teifi; martens are rare, possibly more so than beavers. The Teifi comment can also be read as 'beavers are relatively scarce except on the Teifi'. The comparison of beavers with martens (pine martens?) is particularly interesting, for Lovegrove (2007) writes that at the time of the Tudor Vermin Acts, martens were not as numerous as they had been in the Middle Ages, but they could still be found in every corner of Britain. Harrison's doubts as to whether beavers or martens were the fewer therefore suggests a thinly-spread population for both animals, and for him as for Humphrey Llwyd, the Teifi was the place to find the beavers. However, I have not come across any suggestion that Harrison himself visited Wales, let alone the Teifi.

William Camden (1551 - 1623). In 1586, two years after Powel had published Llwyd's *Cronica Walliae* and the year of the second publication of Harrison's commentary, William Camden published *Britannia*. Camden had been interested since boyhood in antiquities, and on leaving Oxford in 1571 spent three years travelling the country collecting information on topography and antiquities; these travels continued in the holidays after he became a master at Westminster School in London. In 1577 the Antwerp publisher Ortelius, who had published Llwyd's map a few years earlier, made a visit to London in the course of which he met with Camden, and persuaded him to turn his records into the book which appeared some nine years later. Written in Latin, the text was to go through several translations and many editions and expansions in the following decades and centuries, and in his own lifetime Camden continued to travel and to add material to his original text (Piggott 1951). *Britannia* became a major influence on the approach to and understanding of Britain's cultural and landscape heritage.

Camden had an interest in place-names as evidence of former peoples, and set about learning Welsh and Old English to further his researches, Welsh as a living Celtic language relevant to pre-Roman times and Old English as a dead language and therefore more difficult to learn but important for the post-Roman period. However, despite learning some Welsh and travelling in Wales, his passage on the subject of beavers does not suggest any first-hand knowledge of the species. The quotation here is from Gibson's 1695 edition of Camden's text, which has the text for the Welsh counties translated into English by Edward Lhuyd (see below); the passage occurs in relation to the Teifi:

> *For this river abounds with Salmon, and was formerly the only river in Britain, (as Giraldus supposed) that bred Beavers. A Beaver is an amphibious animal, having it's fore-feet like a dog's, but footed behind like a goose; of a dark grey colour; and having an oblong flat cartilaginous tail, which, in swimming, it makes use of to steer it's course. Giraldus makes several remarks upon the subtilty of this creature; but at this time there are none of them found here. (Camden, trans. Edward Lhuyd, 1695)*

In addition to Gerald's account, Camden could have drawn on the beaver paragraph in Humphrey Llwyd's *Description* as published by Powel, or on Harrison's longer account, but his brief description of a beaver's appearance suggests he drew on other sources, yet to be identified. The differences lie in the comparison of beaver feet to those of a goose and a dog (Fig. 4.3), and in saying that the animal was dark grey in colour. He is more emphatic, too, that when he was writing there were no longer beavers on the Teifi.

Fig. 4.3 A month-old beaver eating an apple, showing its hand-like fore feet and big webbed hind feet. *Photo Lars Wilsson 1964.*

Ffigur 4.3 Afanc mis oed yn bwyta afal ac yn dangos ei draed blaen tebyg i ddwylo a'i draed ôl gweog. *Llun Lars Wilsson 1964.*

John Ray (1627 – 1705). Ray (Wray/Raio) was a naturalist who made a significant contribution to the development of systems of classification, and he was an early Fellow of the Royal Society, elected in 1667. He learned Latin at school, and while a Cambridge student added Greek and Hebrew, and he probably acquired some French and Italian (Ewen and Prime 1975). His main interest appears to have been in plants, and from 1658 he made a number of 'botanical journeys' which covered most of Britain (Gilmour 1944), but his work was not confined to botany and in 1693 he published (in Latin) *Synopsis Methodica Animalium Quadrupedum et Serpentini Generis.* Following a brief account of *Hystrix americanus* (the North American porcupine), there are several pages describing *Castor fiber*, the beaver, with p.213 being the most relevant in the present context. Ray held beavers to have been native to the whole of Britain, and he had discussed them with his friend Edward Lhuyd, who also had a strong interest in linguistics (see below). He refers to the Laws of Hywel Dda (Lexico Wallico) and to Gerald of Wales' account of beavers. Most probably through his discussions with Lhuyd, he cites 'Afangc' as the old name of Castor in Wales, and includes a brief mention of beaver-related place-names: '*… et ipse duos tresve lacus novi qui nomen* Llyn yr afangc, *id est, lacus castorei praeferunt.*' (Ray 1693, 213), which may be translated as 'and I have learned of two or three lakes which bear the name *Llyn yr Afangc*, that is, the lake of the beaver' (trans. Edwards/Pryce). Frustratingly, Ray does not say where they were.

Ray was, as far as I can tell, the first to mention *afangc* place-names in print, for although Leland in the earlier 16th century had commented that the town of Beverley in Yorkshire was named after the beaver, his work was not actually published until much later (eg Leland 1774), and he was discussing the English *beuer*, not the Welsh *afangc*. Moreover Ray, who thought that beavers were native to the whole of Britain, does not mention the English place-names, only the Welsh ones. This suggests that he and Edward Lluyd recognised the the significance of beaver place-names independently of Leland. Ray's mention of the *afangc* names in his *Synopsis Methodica Animalium* was to have an important influence on later antiquarian scholarship as well as natural history.

Edward Lhuyd (1660-1709) and Gibson's 1695 edition of Camden's *Britannia*

Edward Lhuyd, described by Stuart Piggott as "a polymath of quite exceptional brilliance" (Piggott 1989, 30), was born and brought up in Shropshire. After probable attendance at Oswestry Grammar School, he became a student at Jesus College Oxford in 1682, and from 1687 he was Assistant Keeper at the Ashmolean, then a very new museum in Oxford. In 1691 he was promoted to Keeper following the retirement of the first keeper Robert Plot. Lhuyd's father lived at Llanforda near Oswestry and his mother at her family home near Tal-y-bont to the northeast of Aberystwyth, a geographical separation which perhaps has a bearing on the beaver story (see Frontispiece map). Lhuyd is thought to have visited his mother's family 'fairly frequently' in his youth, and before he went up to Oxford he was also climbing the hills and mountains of north Wales on botanising expeditions (Williams 2009). On one of these, he discovered the Snowdon Lily, a small plant whose Latin name, *Lloydia serotina,* acknowledges the discoverer (albeit with a different spelling to the one used here). The discovery was made in Cwm Idwal, above Llyn Idwal which feeds into Llyn Ogwen and down Nant Ffrancon, an area known for its beavers and to be examined further below. It is just possible, therefore, that Lhuyd encountered beavers during his travels and explorations.

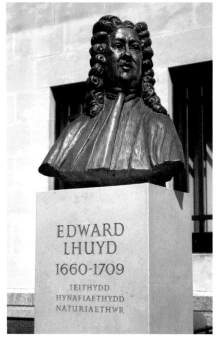

Fig. 4.4 Modern bust of Edward Lluyd, set outside the University of Wales Centre for Advanced Welsh and Celtic Studies, Aberystwyth. *Photo courtesy of CAWCS.*

Ffigur 4.4 Penddelw modern o Edward Lluyd, y tu allan i Ganolfan Uwchefrydiau Cymreig a Cheltaidd Prifysgol Cymru, Aberystwyth. *Llun drwy garedigrwydd CAWCS.*

Avanke, Bever, Castor

It seems probable that Lluyd (Fig. 4.4) spoke Welsh from childhood. By 1690, he had made a statistical analysis of the origins of Welsh vocabulary, the following year he contributed dialect words to the second edition of John Ray's *English Words not Generally Used* (Roberts 2004), and it was not long after this that he discussed beavers in Wales, and their Welsh name *afangc*, with Ray. In fact, Edward Lhuyd could have known Ray from childhood for Ray, who was some thirty years older than Lhuyd, corresponded with Edward Morgan, botanist and gardener for Lhuyd's father, and is possible that he stayed at Llanforda on one or more of his botanising journeys.

Edward Lhuyd's post at the Ashmolean, his interest in linguistics, and in Old Welsh in particular, and his knowledge of natural history and antiquities made him a fitting choice when the young Edmund Gibson was looking for someone to translate and expand the Welsh chapters of Camden's *Britannia*. Lhuyd dealt with all the chapters on Wales, translating Camden's text and compiling additional material for each county, which was placed at the end of the relevant chapter under the heading <u>Additions</u> (Walters and Emery 1977). His translation of Camden's text relating to beavers on the Teifi is quoted above (see section on Camden); his own comments, quoted in the following passage, comes from the <u>Additions</u> which he compiled for Cardiganshire, which was incidentally his mother's native county although her home was well to the north of the Teifi (the opening [C] is Lhuyd's and refers back to the beaver passage in Camden's text):

> *[C] As to the beavers, tho' we may not rely on the authority of Giraldus in many things he relates, (as one who writ in an age less cautious and accurate, and when nothing pleas'd so much as what excited the admiration of the Reader) yet in this case I see but litt'e reason to question his veracity. Moreover, that there were formerly Beavers in this Kingdom, seems much confirmed; in that there are two or three Ponds or Lakes in Wales, well known at this day, by the name of* Lhyn yr Avangk, *i.e. Beaver-pool. The vulgar people of our age, scarce know what creature that* Avangk *was; and therefore some have been perswaded, that 'twas a* Phantom *or* Apparition *which heretofore haunted Lakes and Rivers. As for the name, I take it for granted that 'tis deriv'd from the word* Avonog, *i.e.* Fluviatilis; *as* Lhwynog, *(a Fox) signifies* Sylvaticus, *from* Lhwyn, Sylva. *And for the signification, 'tis not to be controverted; some old Poets so describing it, that I doubt not, but they meant a* Beaver.
>
> *Beside the* Beaver, *we have had some other beasts in Wales...*
>
> (Edward Lhuyd 1695, 645)

Here, Lhuyd draws on his understanding of linguistics and of the development of the Welsh language to show how the name *Afangk* arose, to denote a creature of the river just as *Lhwynog* the fox was the creature of the woods, and he uses his knowledge of the early Welsh poets to argue that the river creature was not some phantom but a real animal, the beaver, which once inhabited Wales. Lhuyd's writings, as published, do not make it clear if he had himself seen beavers or not, nor does he comment on their presence or extinction, but he is confident that he knows what a beaver looks like, and perhaps he did see them during his travels in the Ogwen area. Whether he had come across the two or three place-names during his own travels, or gathered them up from informants, is unclear. However, it is feasible that he had known of them at least from his student days, for one of the place-names lies along a possible route between his father in Oswestry and his mother in northern Cardiganshire, and the other two are in North Wales close to or within his botanising areas (see Pennant below, and section on place-names). It also seems likely, from how he expresses himself, that he knew what *afangk* meant from the outset, maybe from a knowledge of Humphrey Llwyd's *Cronica Walliae* or simply because the word was still in use. This suggestion is reinforced by a letter which I came across recently, written by Lhuyd in 1693, the year that Ray's *Synopsis Methodica Animalium* was published. In it, he mostly discusses local beliefs about the afanc, but he does mention Llyn yr Afanc on the Conwy, and he goes on to say 'You must understand that some take the afanc to be a corporeal demon; but I am sufficiently satisfied that there is an animal of the same name, which is called in English a *bever*, seeing that the term *ceillie'r afanc* signifies *bever stones*.' (quoted in Rhys 1901, p131).

Richard Gough, Edward Lhuyd and the 1789 edition of Camden's Britannia.

Almost a century after Gibson, in 1789, Richard Gough published another new English edition of Camden's *Britannia*. In beaver terms, it is interesting for a new anecdote, apparently from Edward Lhuyd although not in Gibson's 1695 edition. It occurs in Gough's 1789 edition in the <u>Additions</u> for Cardiganshire, in relation to St David and the church at Llandewi-Brefi, where it is said Mr Lhuyd had recorded an inscription over the chancel door of the church:

> *The inhabitants pretend this commemorates a person struck dead by St David for letting loose a most mischievous beaver after it had been with difficulty insnared... The sexton showed him (Mr Lhwyd) a rarity called* Matkornys ych bannog *... adding the fable of the oxen called* Ychen bannog *which drew away a monstrous beaver dead.*   (Gough 1789, 527)

The church is close to a small watercourse, Afon Brefi, which meets the Teifi a couple of kilometres downstream, so beavers in the area are very plausible in the time of St David, who lived in the 6th century AD. However the story, with its mischievous and monstrous beavers, was most probably developed much later, as part of the cult of St David (Edwards and Pryce pers. com.). It may have been stimulated by Gerald of Wales' writings, given the closeness to the Teifi. What is worth noting in the context of 18th century scholarship is the interest which it shows in relation to beavers, as a native animal worthy of notice, both as a local, mischievous animal and as a mythological monstrous beast. According to Chambers

Dictionary of Etymology, 'monstrous' meaning 'huge' or 'enormous' is first recorded early in the 16th century, whereas in the late 13th century it had a sense of 'unnatural' or 'hideous'. Possibly, if oxen were needed to draw the 'monstrous beaver' of Llandewi-Brefi, 'monstrous' was being used in the sense of 'huge', which would put the origin of the latter part of the story relatively late.

Towards the end of the same page, and also emanating from Lhuyd though perhaps tidied up by Gough, is the following passage, a variation on what he had to say on the same subject for Gibson's Camden, adding at the end of the quote another hint of mystery attached to beavers:

> *That the mixture of fable which obtains in Giraldus's writings may not impeach his credit in general, it may not be amiss to observe here, that the existence of beavers antiently in Wales is confirmed by the laws of Howel Dha which fix the price of the skin of the* Llostlydan *or the broadtailed animal at 120 pence, a great sum for that time'. Two or three lakes here still bear the name of* Llyn yr Afangk *or the beaver pool ... Some old poets describe the animal in terms exactly answering to the beaver; though the name is now so little known that some have fancied it a spectre haunting rivers.* (Gough 1789, 527 – 528)

Thomas Pennant (1726 – 1798)

Pennant was born and lived in northeast Wales, at Downing Hall near Whitford in Flintshire. He was a student at Oxford, and emerged with a wide interest in geology, natural history and antiquities. He soon became a prolific and popular writer, and many of his works went through a number of editions. To the general reading public, he was perhaps as well known for his accounts of journeys within Britain as for his works on natural history. The travel books covered Cornwall (1746-47), two journeys to Scotland (1771 and 1774-76) and *A Tour in Wales* published first in 1778-1781. They were well received, and the Scottish *Tours* have recently been re-printed (Withers 1998; Osborne 2000).

Pennant (Fig. 4.5) developed his interest in the natural world from an early age, and he achieved considerable recognition amongst zoologists, publishing on the fauna of Britain and beyond. In 1754 he was elected to the Society of Antiquaries of London, in 1767 to the Royal Society, and in 1768 to the Gentlemen's Society of Spalding. Gilbert White, a fellow member of the Royal Society and author of *The Natural History and Antiquities of Selborne*, was one of his correspondents, and from 1755 he corresponded with Linnaeus, who supported his election in 1757 to the Royal Swedish Society of Sciences in Uppsala. Among his many works, it is *The British Zoology* which is most relevant to beavers in Wales. Pennant was good at providing references for the sources he used, and the successive editions of *The British Zoology* show an interesting expansion of the information on beavers.

Fig. 4.5 Portrait of Thomas Pennant by Thomas Gainsborough, painted in 1776, two years before the publication of *A Tour in Wales*. Note mountainous landscape in the background. *Photo courtesy of Amgueddfa Cymru - National Museum Wales.*

Ffiger 4.5 Portread o Thomas Pennant gan Thomas Gainsborough, a baentiwyd yn 1776, ddwy flynedd cyn cyhoeddi *A Tour in Wales*. Sylwer ar y dirwedd fynyddig yn y cefndir. *Llun drwy garedigrwydd Amgueddfa Genedlaethol Cymru*

The British Zoology was first published in 1766, as an unwieldy folio volume (approx. 52cm high by 36cm wide), with accompanying extra plates. The copy in the British Library is inscribed, presumably in Pennant's own hand, 'Presented by the Author Dec. 2nd 1769'. The next page has a quotation (in Latin) from Camden's *Britannia,* written in the same hand and suggestive of Camden's influence on Pennant. Within the main printed text, at the end of the section on the Otter (p.32-33 plus otter plate), Pennant wrote a short paragraph on Beavers:

> *Beavers, which are also amphibious animals, were formerly found in* Great-Britain; *but the breed has been extirpated many ages ago: the latest account we have of them, is in* Giraldus Cambrensis*, *who travelled through* Wales *in 1188: he gives a brief history of their manners; and adds, that in his time they were found only in the river Teivi; two or three lakes in that principality, still bear the name of* Llyn yr afangc, *or the beaver lake; which is a further proof, that these animals were found in different parts of it†.*
>
> * *Girald. Camb. Itin. P.178, 179.*
>
> † *Raii Syn. quad. 213.*

(Pennant 1766, 33)

In 1768, a second edition of *British Zoology* was published, in four small volumes rather than one very large one, and much easier to handle. The British Library copy has Joseph Banks' bookplate, and it is inscribed 'The Gift of my Esteemed Friend the Author Thos. Pennant Esq.'; both Banks and Pennant were Fellows of the Royal Society, and they seem to have known and respected each other's work. As in the first edition, the paragraph on Beavers follows the Otter text, now with another sentence added at the end, with a reference:

Avanke, Bever, Castor

But we imagine they must have been very scarce even in earlier times; for by the laws of Hoel dda, the price of a beaver's skin (Croen Llostlydan†) was fixed at one hundred and twenty pence, a great sum in those days.

† Llostlydan, that is, the broad tailed animal. Leges Wallicae *261.*

The 1776 edition of *British Zoology* is identified on the title page as the Fourth Edition; I have not been able to find a copy of the third edition, if indeed there was one. The fourth has further additional text on beavers, and a few minor amendments. The full paragraph, still appended to the Otter, reads as follows (I have underlined changes and new text):

Beavers, which are also amphibious animals, were formerly found in Great Britain*; but the breed has been extirpated many <u>years</u> ago: the latest account<u>s we have of them, is in</u>* Giraldus Cambrensis†*, who travelled through* Wales *in 1188: he gives a brief history of their manners; and adds, that in his time they were found only in the river Teivi; two or three <u>waters</u> in that principality, still bear the name of* Llyn yr afangc**, or the beaver lake; which is a further proof, that these animals were found in different parts of it: <u>I have seen two of their supposed haunts; one in the stream that runs through</u>* Nant Frankon*<u>; the other in the river</u>* Conway <u>*a few miles above*</u> Llanrwst*<u>; and both places in all probability has formerly been crossed by Beaver dams</u>. But we imagine they must have been very scarce even in earlier times; by the laws of* Hoel dda*, the price of a beaver's skin* (Croen Llostlydan)†* was fixed at a hundred and twenty pence, a great sum in those days.*

† Giraldus Cambren Itin 178, 179

****Raii Syn. Quad.213.*

† Llostlydan, that is, the broad tailed animal. Leges Walliae *261*

These extracts show that between preparing the first and second editions of *British Zoology*, Pennant had become aware of the relevance of the Laws of Hywel Dda, and during the decade between the second and fourth editions, he had visited both the Conwy 'Beaver Pool' and Nant Ffrancon (Fig. 4.6) having known at least since the first edition that such places existed somewhere in Wales. The small change of wording in the fourth edition, from the 'two or three lakes' to 'two or three waters' and use of the word 'haunts' rather than anything more specific, show Pennant being careful to give an accurate account, for his site visits had revealed that neither the Conwy nor the Nant Ffrancon beaver-places were lakes, as suggested by Lhuyd and Ray, but flowing water. It is likely that Pennant went to the sites during the three journeys which he made between 1773 and 1776 and published as *A Tour in Wales* (2 vols, 1778 and 1781). In the meantime, before the *Tour* came out, preparation of the fourth edition of *British Zoology* had given him the opportunity to amend and expand the beaver text.

Fig. 4.6 Looking northwards down Nant Ffrancon, one of the two 'supposed haunts' of beavers mentioned by Thomas Pennant in the 4th edition of *British Zoology*.

Ffigur 4.6 Edrych tua'r gogledd i lawr Nant Ffrancon, un o ddau leoliad i afancod yn ôl pob sôn, fel y crybwyllwyd gan Thomas Pennant ym mhedwerydd argraffiad *British Zoology*.

Pennant's companion during the Welsh journeys was a near neighbour, the Reverend John Lloyd, whose home was at Caerwys, within three miles or so of Downing Hall (see frontispiece map). Lloyd was known as a fluent Welsh speaker, and he may well have contributed to Pennant's growing fund of information about beavers. For example, Pennant's mention of beaver dams in the fourth edition of *British Zoology* may have been prompted by a discussion with Lloyd of the Nant Ffrancon place-name *Sarn yr Afangc*, interpreted in *A Tour in Wales* as 'the beavers' dam':

> *Nant Frankon is a tremendous glen, or rather chasm, bounded by these and other lofty rocks. In the bottom is a narrow tract of meadowing, watered by the* Ogwen, *which at the end tumbles out of* Llyn Ogwen *down the rude front of the* Benglog. *In one part it is called* Sarn yr Afangc, *or the* Beavers Dam, *another proof of the former existence of those animals in our country.*

(Pennant 1784, vol.2 Continuation/part2, 299 – [nb in this edition the pagination of vol.2 is faulty, running from 1-191 for part 1 and 184 – 487 for Continuation]).

The relevance of the *afangc* place-names to the presence of beavers in Wales is explored further in Chapter 5. What is significant here is Pennant's certainty that, in his own time, beavers no longer existed in Wales, or indeed anywhere in Britain. He was in the habit of gathering information from local sources during his journeys, and it seems that along his routes he had not encountered any suggestion of beavers still living in the vicinity of his travels.

It is also interesting that he takes it for granted that when the beavers were present, they would have made dams, even on the Conwy. In 1765, during his European travels, Pennant had met the French naturalist the Comte de Buffon, well known for his *Histoire Naturelle* in which he wrote at some length about the beavers of Europe and North America. Buffon was intrigued that beavers, like humans and bees, would come together for common projects, such as building a dam or a 'bourgade' (group of huts), but they only did this when they were free of human pressure and congregated in vast numbers, which for Buffon meant in North America but not in western Europe. All our European beavers, he wrote, are solitary burrow-dwellers who, by implication, built neither dam nor lodge (Buffon 1760). Buffon himself had a young Canadian beaver, which he wrote about; it seems to have led a very solitary life, with little chance to build anything. Buffon's views on beaver activity had an immediate influence on the general understanding or, rather, mis-understanding of European beavers, that has lasted to the present in some quarters, yet Pennant did not succumb to the eminent naturalist's views on this matter. Both in *British Zoology* and in *A Tour in Wales*, he offers no hint of a doubt that the beavers of Wales built dams. It is possible that during his continental travels he had seen beavers living on small rivers and streams, where dams would be likely, for although beavers were becoming scarce in many regions by the mid 18th century, Wilson could write a hundred years later that on the continent they were still more widely distributed than most people realised (Wilson 1858). However, I have not come across any comment in Pennant's writings to suggest that he had seen dams built by European beavers, so his confidence that the beavers of Wales would have built dams may have had another source, his correspondence with other scientists such as Linnaeus in Sweden perhaps.

William Owen Pughe (1759-1835) and oral traditions

In 1793 William Owen, who was later to take the surname Pughe (he is often referred to in the literature as Owen Pughe, and I will do the same here), published the first part of *A Welsh and English Dictionary*, covering the letters A–D. The full two-volume dictionary did not appear until 1803 (Williams G.J. 2009). The 1793 volume is not paginated, nor are the entries in strictly alphabetical order. The beaver has a couple of entries, as *azanc* and as *avanc*, five pages apart. The first reads:

> *Azanc….An amphibious animal, once in some of the rivers of this island:*

supposed to be the Llostlydan, or the beaver.

Azanc ni thynir o anozyn dwvyr.

The beaver cannot be drawn from the deep water.

L. G. Cothi

The second reads:

> *Avanc – A beaver. This animal was common in Britain, as is manifest from the Welsh Laws: and we have the authority of Giraldus Cambrensis of its being found in the river Teifi in his time. It is also called Llostlydan and Azanc. It has been seen in Nant Ffrancon in Caernarvonshire in the memory of man.*
>
> A vac o`r zacar aren
>
> A lwnc hi val avanc hen
>
> *What is from the smiling earth she swalloweth like the old beaver.*

T. Aled

It is possible that Cothi and Aled, the two poets quoted by Owen Pughe to illustrate the use of *Azanc/avanc,* are the 'old poets' that Edward Lhuyd referred to. Lewys Glyn Cothi was a poet of the 15th century, while Tudor Aled was active in the late 16th and earlier 17th century, so the latter was not so very 'old' when Edward Lhuyd was writing.

The second entry is particularly interesting for its almost throw-way sentence before the quotation – beavers seen in Nant Ffrancon in the memory of man. Unfortunately, Owen Pughe does not say how he knows this, and I have not come across any earlier mention. However, in the 1860s in *Curiosities of Natural History,* Frank Buckland wrote 'Beavers have not long been extinct in England. … I have heard on good authority that beavers were killed in Wales in the time of Oliver Cromwell. Still I imagine they were never very common…' (Buckland 1863, 90). Buckland, who was well-known as a naturalist, author and Fisheries Inspector, is as annoying as Owen Pughe in not saying who his 'good authority' was, and it could of course have been Owen Pughe himself, or they drew on a common but unidentified source, or the two claims of recent beaver presence may be quite unrelated. I have suggested elsewhere (Coles 2006, 184) that Owen Pughe's 'memory of man' might go back to the mid-to-later 17th century, which would overlap with the 1650s, Buckland's 'time of Oliver Cromwell'. This would indicate that beavers were still present in Wales well after the Middle Ages.

It may be significant that England and Scotland also have oral traditions of beaver presence in living memory, in Scotland as in Wales suggesting a beaver presence in the mid-17th century, and in England a century later (Coles 2006, 182-185). The geographical spread of the three traditions, which are apparently independent of each other, hints at the late survival of several isolated beaver populations. There is also documentary evidence from Bolton Percy in Yorkshire for bounty being paid on a beaver in 1789 (Coles 2006, 187-

190); the animal probably came from the lower reaches of the river Wharfe, which bounds the parish of Bolton Percy. As we have seen, it is likely that the last beaver populations survived either in big rivers such as the Wharfe, where they had no need to make dams and could live largely out of the sight of humans, or in the remote headwaters of a catchment. For Wales, Buckland's comment indicates the possible 17th century killing of beavers for bounty, with no indication as to where, their territories maybe known only to skilful trappers. Owen Pughe, on the other hand, specifies Nant Ffrancon as a place where beavers had endured, and Pennant likewise held that they had been on the Ogwen although gone before his own time.

A damper on the afangc

In the late 18th and early 19th century there were several others who commented on the presence of beavers in Wales. They added little new information, but one of the commentators in particular had an influence on the subsequent understanding, or rather yet another mis-understanding, of beaver behaviour in Britain, and the slow but promising development of interest in beavers, outlined above, began to falter. Richard Colt Hoare was the perpetrator of this reversal, through his 1804 translations of Gerald of Wales' *Itinerary* and *Description*, which were popular and often quoted by others. In his editorial comments (used here as quoted by Meyrick in 1808; the 1908 Everyman edition gives only an abbreviated footnote) he was dismissive of *avanc/afangc* as meaning beaver, particularly as Owen Pughe had said the *afangc* had been seen in Nant Ffrancon within the memory of man. Colt Hoare thought this most unlikely, leading him to argue that *afangc* was an obsolete or local name for otter. As a result, although they continued to be mentioned in passing by some authors, the *afangc* place-names fell out of discussion and investigation; as recently as the late 20th century, and for reasons similar to those given by Colt Hoare, Aybes and Yalden decided not to include the *afanc/afangc* names in their survey of beaver place-names in Britain (1995, 215). Before the 19th century was out, however, one wealthy and enterprising person had brought beavers back to Wales.

The Marquis of Bute and Cardiff Castle

In this survey of beavers in Wales, a pioneering attempt at reintroduction has a character all of its own. It stems from human activity that resulted in a brief sojourn in Cardiff for a pair of beavers, leaving behind a patchy written record together with a number of tangible reminders. Plans for the beavers' visit began in 1872, so far as we know, when the 3rd Marquis of Bute began a correspondence with Frank Buckland. Bute was the youthful and extremely wealthy owner of Cardiff Castle, which he had inherited from his father in 1848 when he was but a year old. In 1865 he began a massive restoration of the castle in the Victorian Gothic Revival style, under the direction of William Burges; another of his projects was the re-introduction of beavers to Scotland, on his island of Bute on the west coast. Buckland we have already met, as the man who said that beavers were killed in Wales in the time of Oliver Cromwell, but failed to say where the information came from. He was the son of Dean Buckland of geological and archaeological renown, and a well-known and popular naturalist, a prolific author, member of the Acclimatisation Society, and generally something of a non-conformist. The Marquis asked Buckland to import some live beavers for him to 'turn out' on his Scottish island, and this in due course happened, resulting in beavers living there in a large enclosure for some fifteen years (for more detail of the Scottish end of the story, see Coles 2006, 93-94, and Conroy, Kitchener and Gibson 1998). The importing of the beavers began with two pairs that arrived in 1874, both probably acquired from mainland Europe. One pair was delivered to Cardiff, where the Marquis kept them for a while. Buckland quotes Bute's own observations as follows:

> *Two of the animals were for a long time shut up in a part of the battlements of the castle at Cardiff, where I had a temporary pond built for them, and could watch them very well, which I did. They would often come out and sit upon the edge of the water, grooming their coats with their forepaws. The action was something between a cat washing, and a monkey scratching itself. They would scratch their heads, and then rub their faces with both paws. The effect was extremely grotesque, very much heightened by the creatures' imperturbable look of stupid gravity. On these occasions I always observed a peculiar action, which I never doubted was that of taking the castoreum on their paws and lubricating their bodies with it.*

(Bute, quoted by Buckland 1887, 277).

Later in 1874 this pair and another two beavers were sent to Scotland, presumably by rail, and released in the island enclosure. They seem to have been quite active in their first weeks, but did not thrive and either escaped or were found dead. In 1875 more beavers were imported, and provided the basis of a population that flourished for a number of years.

The Marquis's interest in beavers is commemorated in the decoration of several of the rooms in Cardiff Castle, which I visited in 2009. The 'beaver' decoration was executed between 1874 and 1880 (Matthew Williams pers. com.), and appears to have been based on studies of the pair that were kept there. The earliest example, from 1874, consists of three beavers carved over the fireplace in Lord Bute's first-floor sitting room. Below gilded mirror-work that throws light back into the room, the mantelpiece is carved with ornate scrolling leaves on which are set four shields with three beavers in between them. The left-hand beaver, associated with a newt, holds a short branch; the middle one, associated with a tortoise, is looking out at the viewer, while the right-hand one, associated with a frog and holding what may be an apple, is looking skywards. All three have a cheerful look about them.

From the sitting room, a spiral staircase leads down to a small hallway with three doors off, each with a decorative panel over the door. The central panel, above the door to the library (Fig. 4.7), shows a woman in medieval dress holding a shield, with a dark red lion rampant rising from a golden helmet to her left and to her right a tree with a thick brown trunk draped with a broad golden band. A beaver, who is somewhat larger than the lion, sits happily nibbling away at something. Within the library itself are walnut bookcases made in 1880, and generously decorated with carved foliage and animals. The bookcases, which stand at right angles to the walls, are divided into two bays on each side. On one side of one of the bookcases the pillars carved on the two end boards and the middle divider are topped by beavers, all carved to the same pattern based on an original by Thomas Nicholls. They are sitting up nibbling at a stick held in their front paws, scaly flat tail curled round to show at the front. The marquis's own crest is carved on the end board, perhaps an indication of his special interest in the species (Matthew Williams pers. com.).

Fig 4.7 Cardiff Castle. Panel above a door to the Library.

Fig 4.7 Castell Caerdydd. Panel uwch ben y drws i'r Llyfrgell.

Taking the spiral staircase up rather than down from the sitting room, it opens onto the battlements, into the Roof Garden. This is not a garden in the usual sense, but an extraordinary open-roofed room where a rectangular paddling-pool takes up most of the floor space (Fig. 4.8). Inspired perhaps by Pompeii, the formality of the rectangular room and pool is offset by the riot of colour and materials used in its decoration. The tiled walls are covered with scenes from the life of the prophet Elijah, below which runs a tiling frieze of white animals on a terracotta background. The tiled sides of the pool carry aquatic foliage and its mosaic base is scattered with fallen-leaf motifs. Bronze plant troughs stand at each corner and towards one end there is a fountain, consisting of a circular bronze basin with a bronze column rising from its centre, both decorated with scattered plant and animal bas-reliefs. The column carries a smaller basin mid-way up, with shields and mythical beasts on its side and a castle-like feature in the centre; mid-way between this and the top of the column are four outward-facing beavers each clutching a large fish in its forepaws.

The fishes' mouths are the spouts of the fountain. The beavers look very determined and a bit desperate, holding the hose-pipe fish like firemen who are not yet sure they can put out a conflagration, but willing to do their best (Fig. 4.9). Originally, the fountain was topped by another bronze beaver, now lost. Along one wall of the room there are two arched bronze doors with bas-relief decoration; the right-hand door shows a window or gate with a beaver behind it, peering out through one of the panels, with a woven fence visible in the background (Fig. 4.10).Perhaps this represents one of the pair of beavers in their Cardiff Castle home.

Fig. 4.8 Cardiff Castle. The Roof Garden, inspired by Pompeii, by Mendelson's *Elijah*, and by the Marquis of Bute's pair of beavers.

Ffigur 4.8 Castell Caerdydd. Gardd y To, a ysbrydolwyd gan Pompeii, gan *Elijah* Mendelson a chan bâr o afancod Marcwis Bute.

The lavish character of the Cardiff Castle beaver evidence, and the investment that went into its production in terms of technical and artistic skill, are quite disproportionate to the brief visit paid by just one pair of beavers in the mid 1870s. However, the evidence is perhaps a fair reflection of the cost of the visit for the humans involved, in terms of the time and effort required to capture them in Germany and bring them live and in good condition to Wales, and in terms of the monetary cost to the Marquis. More definitely, the evidence reflects Bute's strong interest in beavers and their return to Britain. It is ironic that, by comparison, there is hardly any tangible material evidence left for the beavers' presence on the Isle of Bute. In its own way, the story of Bute's beavers serves as a reminder of the potential disjunctions that can exist between human motives and interests, their consequent activities, and the resulting archaeological and historical record.

Fig. 4.9 Cardiff Castle. The fountain beavers, improbably holding fish that will spout water for the fountain (beavers are vegetarian and do not catch fish).

Ffigur 4.9 Castell Caerdydd. Afancod y ffynnon yn dal pysgod, helfa annhebygol, a fydd yn chwistrellu dŵr ar gyfer y ffynnon (mae afancod yn llysieuwyr ac nid ydynt yn dal pysgod).

Fig. 4.10 Cardiff Castle. Detail of a bronze panels in the Roof Garden, showing a somewhat desolate-looking beaver about to eat the bark off a branch.

Ffigur 4.10 Castell Caerdydd. Manylder y panelau efydd yng Ngardd y To yn dangos afanc sy'n edrych braidd yn unig ar fin bwyta rhisgl oddi ar gangen.

CHAPTER 5

BEAVER PLACE-NAMES AND A SEARCH
FOR NEW BEAVER FIELD-EVIDENCE

Despite the many decades of neglect which followed Pennant's innovative place-name fieldwork, a case can be made for taking beaver place-names in Wales seriously. As discussed in the previous chapter, those who first indicated that *afangc* meant 'beaver' were accomplished scholars. Humphrey Llwyd and Edward Lhuyd were familiar with Welsh, Latin and English, and Edward Lhuyd was a pioneer of linguistic studies. Both of them, Humphrey in the mid-16th century and Edward in the late 17th century, asserted that the Welsh *afangc* was the same animal as the English 'beaver'. Edward's near contemporary John Ray, and Thomas Pennant in the later decades of the 18th century, were both experienced naturalists, and they accepted this equation. Furthermore, Edward Lhuyd and Thomas Pennant in particular were keen travellers and recorders of topography, natural history and antiquities. It is unlikely that any of these men completely mis-read the evidence when they equated *afangc* with 'beaver' and proposed 'beaver-pool' as the meaning of *Llyn yr Afangc*. In addition, the oral traditions and other evidence discussed above suggest that beavers survived in Britain well beyond the medieval period. In Wales, as reported by Owen Pughe in the late 18th century, beavers had been seen in Nant Ffrancon within living memory.

All these factors convinced me that the *afangc* place-names of Wales would be as worthy of investigation as the English beaver place-names such as Bardale, Beaverbrook and Beverly. The researched that followed, on the Welsh place-names, has been based on two approaches, both involving field visits. The first consisted of an evaluation of the place-name locations as potential beaver habitat, and the second a search for direct evidence of their former presence.

As seen in earlier chapters, the direct evidence for a former beaver presence has usually come in the form of recognisable beaver bones or beaver-gnawed wood, and occasionally relic beaver structures. In Wales, soil conditions are generally not favourable to the survival of bone. Wood might survive within contexts where there has been continuous undisturbed water-logging, but recognition of the beaver gnaw-marks is also necessary, and has been rare to non-existent until recently. With small likelihood, therefore, of beaver bone or gnawed wood having been recorded within the place-name locations, what was needed was a broader range of evidence. It could, for example, include a search for palaeoenvironmental evidence, such as the beetle *Platypsyllus* which is specific to beavers (Kitchener 2001, 103); its identification in sediments would imply that beavers had also been present. The sediments themselves, that accumulate within a beaver territory, present a complex mix of indicators of disturbance and deposition, and fast and slow water flow which could potentially be characterised and recognised as indicative of beavers. Very recently, work on sediment cores taken at the edge of the Iron Age wetland village of Black Loch of Myrton in southwest Scotland (Crone *et al.* in press), has revealed the survival of sedimentary ancient DNA (so called aDNA) from beavers, dated to around 100 BC (Brown pers. com. 2018) This is not so surprising given that beavers live and die predominantly in and around water, and it opens up a whole new avenue of research into the history and ecology of beavers. This sort of evidence requires specialist investigation, rather than identification during a field visit, and it has not as yet been undertaken in relation to the place-name contexts. However, it is a rapidly expanding field, and it will be interesting to see what results emerge in the next few years in relation to beavers.

Fig. 5.1, Beaver canals, such as this one leading to a feeding area, silt up when the beavers stop using them, just one of the categories of evidence for their former presence in the landscape.

Ffigur 5.1 Mae camlesi afancod, fel yr un yma sy'n arwain i ardal fwydo, yn llenwi gyda llifwaddod pan mae afancod yn rhoi'r gorau i'w defnyddio, dim ond un o'r categorïau o dystiolaeth o'u presenoldeb yn y dirwedd ar un adeg.

There is one category of evidence that beavers leave behind which is relatively easy to identify and has a high chance of survival, namely the features that they create in the river banks and on the adjoining land. Just as a humanly-dug pit or post-hole accumulates sediment and is later identified by archaeologists thanks to its differential fill, so too a beaver-dug channel (Fig. 5.1), burrow or den fills up following abandonment. Later, it may be revealed by erosion, showing up through differences in colour or texture. In particular, a beaver feature may be revealed by differential erosion of the river bank, with the generally less compact fill of the burrow or channel being washed away before the surrounding matrix crumbles too, thus exposing the beaver-dug void. The burrows of other species such as fox and badger may also survive, so it is important to check size, shape and location to correctly attribute a void to its digger. Foxes and badgers make smaller burrows than beavers, and they would not normally be found in ground that was waterlogged at the time of digging.

Many local factors influence both the relationship of beaver features to the flow of water and the extent of burrow-and-den complexes. A similar diversity of factors affects present-day erosion. This means that a freshly-exposed bank face might reveal a long oblique section across a burrow rather than a neat cross-section, or it might clip the convergence of two burrows on a den floor, for example. Georges Érome, a French engineer with a strong interest in beavers, provides a range of examples in his doctoral thesis (Érome 1982). Some years ago, I decided to search for such features in the main beaver place-name locations in Wales, and made several field visits in 2008 and 2009, assisted by a number of people with local knowledge. As well as the search for potential beaver features, we made a general assessment of each location as a place for beavers to live.

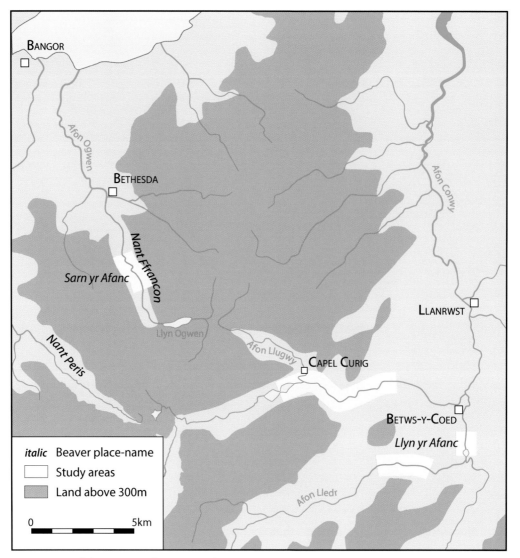

Fig. 5.2 Map of the Conwy and Ogwen catchments.
Ffigur 5.2 Map o ddalgylchoedd Conwy ac Ogwen.

Avanke, Bever, Castor

Beaver families do not, on the whole, live in isolation from each other despite their fierce territoriality. Around a lake or along a water-course, there will be a number of territories, separated by zones of reduced beaver activity which adjacent families may use from time to time. Where a place-name location has attributes attractive to beavers, I have therefore considered also the broader riverine setting. This has included exploration of tributaries, and some consideration of catchments and the potential beaver routes between them. The following account of the fieldwork results begins with the Conwy catchment (Fig.5.2), where Thomas Pennant made what was probably his first inspection of a beaver place-name site.

Llyn yr Afanc, Afon Conwy and tributaries

Llyn yr Afanc, the Beavers' Pool, is a broadening of the river Conwy above Betws y Coed, immediately below the bridge which carries the A470 road over the river (I suggested the wrong bridge in Coles 2006). The site is promising in beaver terms. The pool (Fig.5.3a) is broad and deep, with high banks that are rocky in places but interspersed with potential 'soft' sites where beavers could dig themselves an underground den. The depth of water is sufficient to cover and protect their burrow entrances and dens at all times, except perhaps during a very severe drought. There was therefore no need for the beavers to build dams. At the downstream end, where the big pool gives way to riffles, there is a mid-stream island. The pool itself provides about 250m of bank feeding area, and the island below with its two river channels provides another 450m or so, all within about 200m swimming distance of the middle of the pool.

If, in the past, generations of beavers had fed on the bankside vegetation, a zone of shrubby browse (beaver-pasture) would have developed, fringing the pool and very different to the present trees. A beaver family with access to some 700m of good twiggy browse around the pool and the island would have found enough food without having to fell mature trees. The family could have slept safe and dry in their bank-dens, except perhaps during extreme floods. A recent example of severe flooding having a dire effect on the local beaver population comes from the Rhône valley in 2003, when many beavers drowned in the vast, fast-flowing spread of waters, and it took a long time for the disrupted families to re-settle and re-establish their territories. Very young beavers in the den, in early summer, are particularly at risk of drowning. Similarly severe flooding could have happened from time to time on the Conwy, with new beaver families settling on the Pool once the local population had recovered from the catastrophe.

But such extreme floods are rare events, and Llyn yr Afanc appears to be aptly named, a good site for beavers for many generations at a stretch, and a place where they may have survived into relatively recent times. This suggestion is supported by a map dated 1839, in the third edition of Bingley's *Excursions in North Wales* (of which more below). The relevance here is that, clearly marked on the map to the west of the Conwy downstream of Waterloo Bridge are the words 'Beaver Grove' (Fig.5.3b).

Fig. 5.3 a) Llyn yr Afanc, the pool below the road bridge which carries the A470 over Afon Conwy.

Ffigur 5.3 a) Llyn yr Afanc, y pwll islaw'r bont ffordd sy'n cludo'r A470 dros Afon Conwy.

Fig. 5.3 b) 'Beaver Grove' marked on 1839 map close to Llyn yr Afanc.

Ffigur 5.3 b) 'Beaver Grove' wedi'i farcio ar fap o 1839 yn agos at Lyn yr Afanc.

It is likely that beaver territories were established along the river above and below Llyn yr Afanc. Downstream, high banks and deep pools would have provided many places for a secure den, with plenty of vegetated shoals and lower banks for the beavers to feed from.

Conwy tributaries

Afon Lleder is a west-bank tributary of the Conwy, joining the larger river shortly above Llyn yr Afanc; when beavers were living in and around the Conwy pool, it is likely that other families were settled along the Lleder. A stretch of about two and a half kilometres was surveyed from the south bank, working downstream from Pont y Pant to Pont Gethin railway viaduct (see Fig. 5.2). The river varies from pool-like areas of moderately deep water, sometimes enhanced by humans for fishing purposes, to waterfalls and narrow gorges, interspersed with stretches of placid water, long rock-strewn rushing shallows and occasional rapids. For beavers, the potential offered by the river would have varied considerably within short distances. Nowhere would have been impassable, by land if not by water, but rapids, waterfalls and gorges would, on the whole, have been places to pass through and maybe to feed along the bank, while territories were established and burrows and dens excavated where it was easier for the beavers to dig. As along the Conwy, floods no doubt posed a hazard at times, depending on their severity and duration, and the time of year.

Along the calmer stretches of the Lleder, bank height is as much as one metre in places, with soils suitable for burrows and dens; given the likelihood of water levels often being higher than during my field visits, it is likely that the beavers built above-ground lodges as well as earth-fast dens. In addition, some of the tumbles of boulders to the side of the river could have sheltered dens, as they do today in central Brittany, at the lower end of the Ellez beaver territories where the river flows through a strew of enormous boulders. Sometimes, if you peer through the gap between two boulders lying embedded in the slopes above the river, or hold a camera into the gap and take a photo, you will see beaver-gnawed sticks and perhaps the shredded wood-shavings that make up beaver-bedding. Between the den and the river, treacherous ankle-twisting holes in the ground show where the roof of a beaver burrow has fallen in, a reminder that the dens are reached by hidden, underground burrows that the beavers enter from below water.

The width and the flow rate of the Lleder are within the range that beavers are capable of damming. A likely location for a beaver dam in the past is where pools now give way to riffles; the dam is relatively easy to anchor at such a point, and it will enhance the pool for greater security of den entrance; relic beaver features such as dens and burrows are most likely to be associated with such pools. At the time of the survey, visibility was generally good, and several freshly eroded or otherwise bare sections of the north bank were observed, but without any clear beaver features being identified within it. This does not mean that beavers never lived here, simply that at the time of the survey there were no exposed features – erosion is constant, though not at a steady rate, and features once exposed will be eroded out and for a while easy to identify, but then lost through further erosion. It is important, therefore, to record exposed features immediately, if only by taking a photo and making a note of the location.

Within the surveyed length of the Lleder, at the lower end of a low-gradient stretch of water, there is a side channel, dry when visited, which defines a long, narrow river island. The island consists of shillet shoals of variable height intermixed with finer deposits and overlain by forty to sixty centimetres of soil, and it supports oak trees with alder along the riverside bank. The trees look to be forty to eighty years old which, together with the depth of soil and flourishing bluebells, suggests at least several decades of development unhindered by whatever floods there have been. For several metres along the landward edge of the island, differential erosion has created a horizontal linear void similar in character and dimensions to a beaver burrow, which would be about thirty to sixty centimetres across, and may have been dug to provide safe access to a feeding area (Fig. 5.4). The tunnel-void looks to be in current use as an animal pathway, for species of rabbit to fox size, and one more recent burrow of a smaller animal, such as a water vole, was visible in its wall, but the void does not appear to owe its origin to these present-day users. Instead, it looks to pre-date the current channel, and may first have been made before the current island was isolated, or when a different pattern of channels and islands existed. Beavers are apt to cause local changes when they settle in the backwaters of larger streams and rivers, and during the Beaver Works Project we recorded one such area of change on the Bes river, where the beaver territory encompassed several islands and a tributary as well as a stretch of the main river. On the Lleder, it may have been beavers that caused the island to form, as well as subsequently burrowing into it.

Fig. 5.4 Afon Lleder side channel, with a possible longitudinal beaver burrow. The main river is in the background.

Ffigur 5.4 Sianel ochr Afon Lleder, gyda thwll afancod hydredol o bosib. Mae'r brif afon yn y cefndir.

Voids are difficult to date, especially when the fill that accumulated once they fell out of use has been washed away. Sometimes, all one can say is that they are more recent than the surrounding sediments. There is no direct proof that the void in the edge of the Lleder island was made by beavers. However, during the Holocene there has been no other native burrowing animal big enough to have made it, that would be active in a place so closely associated with water. The burrow must have flooded every time the river rose to bank height, probably most winters; it could have been dug out by beavers to reach an above-ground lodge, but more probably it was part of an underground and often water-filled route, as found in many European contexts where beavers are well established. It is the sort of feature that warrants further careful investigation, subject to the consent of the landowner, and with the help of an appropriately qualified team.

Afon Llugwy, the next west-bank tributary of the Conwy downstream of Afon Lleder, is within exploration range for the beavers of Llyn yr Afanc. In 2008 and 2009, brief surveys were carried out from the south bank, above and below the A5 road bridge at Tŷ-hyll some five kilometres upstream of the Conwy confluence, and also further upstream at Capel Curig.

Fig. 5.5 Afon Llugwy, a river with potential for beaver settlement.

Ffigur 5.5 Afon Llugwy, afon gyda photensial i afancod ymsefydlu yno.

Above and below the Tŷ-hyll bridge, the Llugwy (Fig. 5.5) has deeper and longer stretches of placid water and higher banks than observed along the Lleder. These would have been good places for beavers to settle, while the intermittent stretches of rocky water, though sometimes long, would not have hindered beaver passage and in many cases the banks would have provided suitable foraging territory. The present river is slightly too wide and strong-flowing for beavers to build any long-lasting dams, except where a river island divides the flow, but they could have made occasional insubstantial dams at the lower end of a pool, for example to raise water levels for extra security when they had kits in the den.

Upstream of the bridge, there is a large cobble island and above that a broad pool; the river banks are perhaps thirty metres apart here, whereas below the bridge the river narrows to about ten metres and deepens. The topography suggests that humans may have made a ford across the wide shallow river before it was bridged, and that beavers may from time to time have dammed all or part of the shallow water-flow. The present island may itself be of recent origin, but its existence suggests there will have been predecessors. Pool, island, beaver dam and human crossing point are factors that would have interacted for thousands of years following the re-colonisation of Wales after the last glaciation. In particular, beaver dams tend to lead to the widening of the dammed watercourse immediately above and below the dam, which may suggest an origin for the pool. Beaver dams themselves are often strong enough to serve as a causeway for human passage (see Fig. 2.5), and the associated widening dissipates the force of the current, another factor promoting long-term human use of the location as a place to cross the river.

At Capel Curig, around the confluence of the Llugwy and Nant Gwyrd, there is a broad and relatively flat area of ground between the two water-courses. A broad pool, fair bank height and indications of former side channels combine to suggest this would have been good beaver territory. In one recently exposed face of the river-bank, differential erosion revealed a complex of voids that may have derived from several episodes of beaver burrowing and den-making, followed by human dumping of rubbish in more recent times.

From Capel Curig upstream to Nant y Benglog, where several streams come together to form the Llugwy, it is unlikely that beavers would have established any permanent territories as the watercourse is narrow, rocky and fast-flowing. There would, however, have been food and temporary sheltering places for solitary beavers, both youngsters and adults, wandering in search of a mate and a place to settle.

Afon Ogwen, in Nant Ffrancon

Afon Ogwen rises within a stone's throw of the Llugwy headwaters in the high flat watershed area of Nant y Benglog (see Fig. 5.2). From here, while the Llugwy heads east to join the Conwy, the Ogwen flows westwards to reach the sea at Bangor (see Fig. 4.6). It originates in a number of small streams feeding into Llyn Ogwen, a lake about 1.5km long and up to 500m wide with a dramatic outfall, tumbling almost 100m down into the valley of Nant Ffrancon. The narrow, steep-sided and flat-bottomed glacial valley leads northeastwards for about four kilometres to Ceunant, after which the spoil heaps of slate quarries now dominate the landscape down to Bethesda. Small-scale quarrying and mining have a very long history in the valley, becoming more organized and intensive from the later 18th century. The main spreads of spoil date to the mid 19th century (Hubback 1987). When Thomas Pennant and William Owen Pughe made their visits in the later 18th century, the spoil heaps and the mining village of Bethesda barely existed, and the valley of Nant Ffrancon extended downstream some one to two kilometres further than today, as it had done since the last ice sheets melted. Pennant, it will be remembered, wrote that 'Nant Frankon is a tremendous glen, or rather chasm…In the bottom is a narrow tract of meadowing, watered by the *Ogwen*' and he added ' In one part it is called *Sarn yr Afangc*, or the *Beavers Dam*, another proof of the former existence of those animals in our country.' (Pennant 1784). Not long after Pennant published *A Tour in Wales*, in 1799-1800, the artist J. M. W. Turner made his own tour of Snowdonia, creating a pictorial record which well conveys the dramatic atmosphere of the valley (Fig.5.6). It is unclear whether the sketch is of Nant Ffrancon or nearby Nant Peris, but a photo taken of Nant Ffrancon a few decades later by Roger Fenton (Fig. 5.7) has a strong similarity, and both add to Pennant's description.

Fig. 5.6 From a 1799-1800 sketchbook of J. M. W. Turner (1775 -1851) held by the Tate Gallery, this image is catalogued as 'Nant Peris looking towards Snowdon (?Nant Ffrancon from Llanlechyd)'. Compare with Fig. 5.7. *Image ©Tate, London 2018.*

Ffigur 5.6 O lyfr braslunio o 1799-1800 gan J. M. W. Turner (1775 -1851) sydd yn Oriel Tate, mae'r llun yma wedi'i gatalogio fel 'Nant Peris looking towards Snowdon (?Nant Ffrancon from Llanlechyd)'. Cymharwch â Ffigur 5.7. *Llun ©Tate, Llundain 2018.*

Fig. 5.7 Photograph of Nant Ffrancon, taken by Roger Fenton in 1857. Note the Blaen-y-nant footbridge over the Ogwen middle left, and the meandering river scattered with islands. The valley changed relatively little in the decades since Pennant and Owen Pughe saw it. *Photo © Royal Photographic Society/National Museum of Science and Media/Science and Society Picture Library.*

Ffigur 5.7 Llun o Nant Ffrancon, a dynnwyd gan Roger Fenton yn 1857. Sylwer ar bont droed Blaen-y-nant dros afon Ogwen yn y canol ar y chwith, a'r afon droellog ag ynysoedd bychain ynddi. Nid yw'r dyffryn wedi newid ryw lawer yn ystod y degawdau ers i Pennant ac Owen Pughe ei weld. *Llun © Y Gymdeithas Ffotograffig Frenhinol / Yr Amgueddfa Genedlaethol ar gyfer Gwyddoniaeth a Chyfryngau / Llyfrgell Lluniau Gwyddoniaeth a Chymdeithas.*

For several millennia after the retreat of the Snowdonian glaciers, Nant Ffrancon above Ceunant was filled by a lake, called Llyn Ffrancon by the modern scholar who identified it (Seddon 1962). Sediments accumulated in the lake basin, fairly quickly thanks to the huge erosion of coarse material off the surrounding mountainous terrain. The shallower waters of the lake margins developed into marshy land, and in due course the lake probably fragmented into a series of smaller pools linked by a multi-channelled Ogwen. It was only in recent times that the present drainage of the valley came in to being, through human intervention in the 19th and 20th centuries. People had visited the valley and perhaps settled there seasonally in the early millennia for hunting and fishing and gathering wild plants. Later, as farmers, they also brought their stock to summer pastures and they quarried for stone and ores. From about 1600 AD, improvements in agriculture and the road network began to make year-round human settlement viable. Beavers would have had no such limitations, and could have established their territories for year-round settlement early in the postglacial period.

Pollen analysis carried out in the later 20th century has indicated that the valley floor and lower slopes were wooded, though not of course where there was open water (Rhind and Jones 2003). It has been suggested that the tree cover would still be there but for humans and their grazing animals, and early signs of openings in the tree cover are attributed to human activity. However, both the pollen analysis and the study of the lake sediments were carried out without any serious thought as to the possible role of beavers in the development of the valley landscape. Beavers are quite capable of creating lakes, if the local topography is favourable. Nant Ffrancon has a shallow gradient, with a fall from the head of the valley to the Ceunant pinch-point, four kilometres downstream, of about twenty metres, a gradient of 1 in 200 or 0.5%. Under these conditions, it would have been possible for beavers to build dams that held back large bodies of water.

Initially, they may have created several major dams, particularly at natural pinch-points as at Ceunant, or where low rock ridges cross the valley as at Tŷ-Gwyn (Fig. 5.8). As the dams expanded, the series of lakes may have merged, only to separate again as the sediments accumulated and marshy land emerged, with the river flowing through multiple channels wending around the natural islands and through the thick marshy vegetation and patches of alder carr. The valley, once dominated by glacial processes, most probably came under strong beaver influence for several millennia following the retreat of the ice sheets. In beaver terms, the valley would have been a good place to live throughout its gradual evolution, with ample marshland vegetation and willow scrub to feed off, and a watercourse that could be dammed where necessary. Initially their dens may have been predominantly protected by building above-ground lodges, but as the valley sediments accumulated, there will have been enough depth in places for sub-surface dens, and a variety of bank-lodges suited to intermediate conditions.

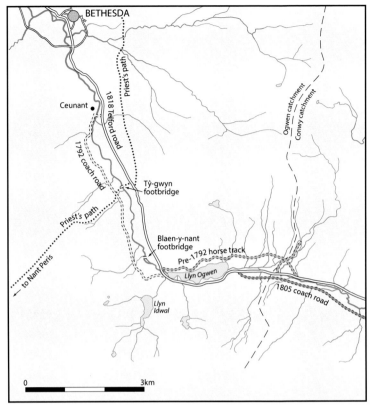

Fig. 5.8 Map of Nant
Ffrancon.

Ffigur 5.8 Map o Nant
Ffrancon.

After many millennia of beaver activity, when Thomas Pennant and then William Owen Pughe recorded their visits to Nant Ffrancon in the late 18th century, the beavers had gone. However, according to Owen Pughe their departure was recent, no more than a few decades, in which case Edward Lhuyd could well have seen them in the late 17th to early 18th century. It may have been the more efficient mining and farming promoted from the mid 18th century onwards by the Pennant family of the Penrhyn estate near Bangor (not related to Thomas Pennant) that put an end to the co-existence of beavers and humans in the valley, and maybe the mining and processing of arsenical ores was a contributing factor. David Hubback, in his 1987 history of Nant Ffrancon, refers to the 19th century exploitation of arsenic ores at Ceunant, with associated human ill health and early deaths, and pollution of the river. Beavers do sometimes live in quite polluted areas, but as and when there was mining that led to arsenical run-off it could well have affected the local beavers.

The Penrhyn estate was sold off in the 1950s, and much of it acquired by the National Trust. In the 1960s the river bed was lowered to reduce flooding, but the flat land either side of the river is still primarily used for pasture, with some tree cover lower down, and management is designed to protect the scientific and conservation value of the remarkable landscape. The Ogwen in Nant Ffrancon is near-perfect for a search for relic beaver features. It has good bank exposures to study and the shifts of the river's course expose different parts of the valley floor, all of which may have seen beaver activity. In other words, the engineering works of the 1960s have not destroyed the potential for beaver evidence to have survived and to be revealed from time to time. The current exposures show variable depths of soil, sometimes overlying peaty deposits, and with influxes of rocky debris brought in by minor tributaries from the steep, bare valley sides.

In May and in August 2008, as part of the same project as the Conwy catchment survey, the central area of Nant Ffrancon was visited, upstream and downstream of the Tŷ-gwyn foot-bridge; riverside visibility was good at the time of the surveys. There are occasional rocky knolls in the valley floor, including one at the foot-bridge which has probably influenced humans in their choice of crossing-point. This knoll is part of a long cross-valley ridge which, prior to the extensive drainage of the valley, provided a valuable dry passage for an historic long-distance human route, known as the Priest's Path, which comes up the valley on the east side, and crosses the river at Tŷ-gwyn to make the steep ascent out of the valley and on to Nant Peris (see map, Fig. 5.8). The 1960s river engineering did not destroy all the local variability and character of the Ogwen, which retains pools and meanders indicative of its former wandering. The width is such that beavers could today build dams across, and they would easily have done so before the engineering tidied up some of the side channels and islands and loops that in human eyes contributed to flooding, but for beavers dispersed the flow, and dissipated its force. It is probable that rapid snow-melt, or a sudden release of water from Llyn Ogwen, would sweep away any dams, but European beavers living in mountainous terrain today will rebuild after such events (see Chapter 1 and Coles 2006, 158), and beavers on the Ogwen would presumably have done the same.

Immediately below the Tŷ-gwyn foot-bridge, the river widens into a deep natural pool, with a rocky knoll exposed at the bridge on the east bank. In 2008, in the earthen bank-face against the rock, a large hollow could be seen, with a lower and an upper cavity (Fig. 5.9; see also Fig. 1.8). The lower cavity looked to be in current use as a shelter for some animal, and possibly it had been recently enlarged by humans for the benefit of otters. The upper cavity was more shallow, with a band of finer deposits leading up to it from the downstream side. Immediately upstream, overlying the rock, there is another slight hollow of similar dimensions. These features could be the remains of a complex of beaver dens that evolved over a long period, and filled with sediments after final abandonment. Subsequently, the fill of the former voids has been eroded out and they have been enlarged at times of severe flooding. Now there is nothing left relating to any beaver occupation that would be suitable for dating. Nevertheless, these features can be interpreted as the relics of beaver activity, and their presence suggests there may be other such complexes within Nant Ffrancon. Their association with the pool is promising, and probably the *Sarn yr Afangc* name reported by Pennant related to successive dams built by the beavers living here, unless it was further upstream at the Blaen-y-Nant footbridge, but I think Tŷ-gwyn is the more likely.

Fig. 5.9 a) Looking downstream from Tŷ-Gwyn footbridge at possible beaver dens.

Ffigur 5.9 a) Edrych i lawr yr afon o bont droed Tŷ-Gwyn ar dyllau afancod posib.

Fig. 5.9 b) Erosion of the river bank has revealed two or three possible dens or burrows, and there has been some recent enhancement by humans, to provide shelter for otters. Scale 25cm.

Ffigur 5.9 b) Mae erydiad glan yr afon wedi datgelu dau neu dri thwll neu wâl bosib, ac mae rhywfaint o wella wedi bod yn ddiweddar gan bobl, er mwyn darparu cysgod ar gyfer dyfrgwn. Graddfa 25cm.

Walking downstream from Tŷ-gwyn, more features could be seen in the exposed banks of the Ogwen. In one place, darkish yellow-brown features stood out from the light brown matrix of the bank face, and a capping of stony material indicated that the features had not been cut from the present surface – in other words, they were not recent in date (Fig. 5.10). The features looked to be more clayey than the surrounding sediments, and all were at much the same level. About one metre below the present ground surface, one segment, about thirty centimetres square, had the size and shape of a small beaver exit path or channel. Further on, more beaver-like features were noted to either side of a sharp bend of the river. Here, the bank faces were higher than upstream, and they showed much variability in colour and texture. Among and below a mass of exposed roots, differential colouring and erosion were apparent, as if there had once been burrows and a den. They lay relatively low in the bank exposure, maybe dug by beavers relatively early in the post-glacial period, before the full sequence of sediment deposition had taken place.

The brief surveys in Nant Ffrancon have shown that the valley would have been very suitable for beaver settlement, and there is no reason to doubt Pennant's proposed meaning of 'Beaver Dam' for *Sarn yr Afangc*. Finding that the valley has possible field evidence for past beaver activity, in the form of relic dens, burrows and channels, adds to the likelihood of a former, well-established beaver population along this stretch of the Ogwen. Furthermore, it is Nant Ffrancon that has the most recent sighting of beavers in Wales, as recorded by William Owen Pughe. It is probable that beavers would have been more obvious to humans here than along the Conwy, as they are likely to have built a number of dams across the watercourse at any one time. It is fitting therefore that Nant Ffrancon itself may be a beaver place-name, 'the name being supposed to be a corruption of *Nant yr Afancwm*, or the Beaver Hollow.' (Barrett-Hamilton and Hinton 1921, 675). Not all scholars accept this interpretation, but whatever the name meant originally I have no doubt that there were beavers in Nant Ffrancon for many thousands of years (Fig. 5.11), and the dam known to humans as *Sarn yr Afangc* was but one of a multitude such dams built by the beavers across the Ogwen.

Fig. 5.10 a Eroded bank of the Ogwen, several hundred metres downstream of the Tŷ-Gwyn footbridge, showing a possible beaver canal which stands out as a dark, roughly rectangular silty patch in a light grey layer. Scale in feet.

Ffigur 5.10 a Glan afon Ogwen wedi erydu, rai cannoedd o fetrau i lawr yr afon o bont droed Tŷ-Gwyn, yn dangos camlas afancod posib sy'n sefyll yn glir fel darn llifwaddodol tywyll, petryal ei siâp yn fras, mewn haen lwyd golau. Graddfa mewn troedfeddi.

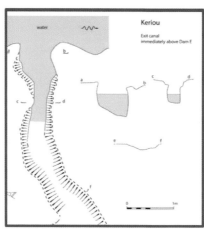

Fig. 5.10 b Left, a beaver canal in Brittany. Right, plan and cross section of a short canal, also in Brittany

Ffigur 5.10 b Ar y chwith, camlas afancod yn Llydaw. Ar y dde, cynllun a thrawsdoriad camlas byr, hefyd yn Llydaw.

Fig. 5.11 Female beaver with two kits, a sight that was once common in Nant Ffrancon.
Photo Mike Symes, Devon Wildlife Trust.

Ffigur 5.11 Afanc benywaidd gyda dau genau, golygfa a arferai fod yn gyffredin ar un adeg yn Nant
Ffrancon. *Llun Mike Symes, Ymddiriedolaeth Natur Dyfnaint.*

The Conwy and Ogwen catchments

The search for beaver field evidence, in the form of relic features excavated in river banks, has been particularly successful along the watercourses associated with the beaver place-names of North Wales. In each area, potential burrows and dens have been observed. The place-name locations, the Beaver Pool on the Conwy and the Beaver Dam (or causeway) in the possible Valley of the Beaver, can be confirmed as good places for beavers to live. What is interesting too is the contrast between the Conwy and the Ogwen in terms of likely beaver visibility to people. In all likelihood, the beavers living in the deep pool on the big river were less evident to humans than those living in the flat valley, where they dammed its narrow river channels, and where the humans probably told each other to cross the wettest part of the valley by walking atop the rocky ridge and the beaver dam. Nevertheless, both places were named by the humans for the beavers living there, so we must suppose that the Conwy beavers were spotted at dawn and dusk, swimming across the pool with a tasty twig clenched in their jaws, or maybe the young ones enjoyed diving under a fisherman's coracle and popping up briefly on the far side to take a look at him. One summer's evening, a small group of us humans paddled along a canal in Sweden just after sunset, hoping to spot a beaver swimming in the distance. We were surprised and delighted when three or four youngsters started playing games around and under the canoes – they seemed to be much less wary of humans in a boat than humans on land.

For the beavers themselves, Nant Ffrancon was perhaps just long enough for three or four families to establish their territories, and along the surveyed stretches of the Conwy and its tributaries the Lleder and the Llugwy there may have been as many as six to eight territories, making perhaps thirty-five to fifty beavers in all. Contact between the Ogwen and Llugwy populations would have been possible, despite the dramatic terrain; the distance between a territory on the Llugwy around Capel Curig and another territory in the upper part of Nant Ffrancon would have been less than ten kilometres by water, with potential temporary resting places along the way. It may or may not be relevant that a monster beaver is said once to have inhabited Llyn Idwal, the glacial lake above Nant Ffrancon that feeds into Llyn Ogwen, a folk memory perhaps of a solitary migrating animal that settled for a while (Fernandez 2012). Today's expanding beaver population in Europe has provided new instances of these solitary individuals that live for years on their own, before a mate comes their way, or they move on, or die. For the overland climb out of Nant Ffrancon, or the descent into the valley, a beaver lured on by the scent of a potential mate could have taken the same west bank route as the present minor road down from Llyn Ogwen. Such contact would have given the two beaver groups a greater chance of survival than if they had been isolated, and might help to explain why the last report of beavers living in Wales comes from this area.

Finding *Llyn yr Afangc* in Montgomeryshire

The person who first drew attention to the location of another of Edward Lhuyd's *Llyn yr Afangc* place-names was the same scholar who doubted that *afangc* meant beaver, and thereby contributed to the assumption of an early beaver decline and extinction from Wales. In his editorial notes to his translation of Gerald of Wales' *Itinerary*, Sir Richard Colt Hoare wrote 'A small lake in Montgomeryshire is called *Llyn yr Afangc*' (Hoare 1806, 56; see also Chapter 4). Unfortunately, he did not give a precise location. In searching the literature, I found that in subsequent decades a number of people referred to the 'small lake in Montgomeryshire', but none of them identified which it was of the several small lakes in the county. Then I found in *A History of British Mammals* that Barrett-Hamilton and Hinton placed the lake between Moat Lane and Llanidloes (1921, vol.II part ii, p.675). Moat Lane today is the road leading south-eastwards across the Severn from Caersws. When Barrett-Hamilton and Hinton were writing, it was also the name of the local railway station, and thus well known to visitors. Llanidloes is the next town upstream, about twelve kilometres distant following the valley floor, and the 'small lake' was therefore close to, though not necessarily within, the Severn valley. There are a number of beaver place-names lower down the Severn, in England and derived from the Anglo-Saxon *beuer/bever* (Coles 2006) and it was an intriguing thought that this river might carry beaver names from two distinct linguistic roots.

In the summer of 2009, we spent a few days exploring this stretch of the Severn valley, assessing it in general terms as an area for beaver settlement, and looking in particular at the 'small lakes' to see which might have been called Beaver Pool. When Hoare first referred to the 'small lake in Montgomeryshire', his wording implied that, unlike the Conwy pool, it was not intimately connected to a river. For this first visit I therefore assumed that the pool did not have to be within the Severn floodplain, but that it would be within a broad band of land between Llanidloes and Caersws/Moat Lane It was unlikely to be one of the man-made reservoirs, although these could not be entirely ruled out as a number of the beaver-named watercourses in England are closely associated with small man-made reservoirs (Coles 2006). The association has come about because, in the context of small watercourses, the prime places for beavers to settle are also prime locations for humans to make reservoirs – in each case, a relatively short dam will make a relatively large pond.

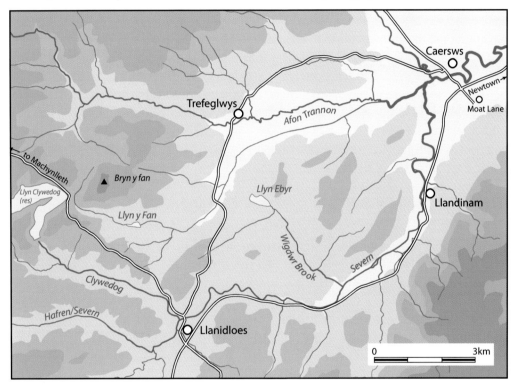

Fig. 5.12) Map of Upper Severn between Llanidloes and Newtown.
Ffigur 5.12) Map o ran uchaf Afon Hafren rhwng Llanidloes a'r Drenewydd.

In the area between Llanidloes and Caersws/Moat Lane there are several bodies of water, just two of which might once have been called *Llyn yr Afangc*, both on the left bank of the Severn looking downstream. One, Llyn Ebyr, lies about three kilometres north of the Severn, to the northeast of Llanidloes. The other, Llyn y Fan, lies two and a half kilometres northwest of Llanidloes (Fig. 5.12). Whilst these two lakes were given priority, we visited a number of the other small to medium bodies of water in the area, but none looked worthy candidates for the name of *Llyn yr Afangc*.

On visiting Llyn y Fan, it immediately became obvious that it is part of the now-derelict Van Mines. This complex was at its height of activity as a lead mine in the latter half of the 19th century, when the mines were powered by water wheels and by steam, both of which called for a water supply. Llyn y Fan itself is a man-made reservoir, held back by a massive wall and fed by streams coming off Bryn y Fan. Although built on an industrial scale, the reservoir's location may well have been chosen to take advantage of topography once exploited by beavers for their own pool. In other words, the 19th century industrial origin of the present lake does not preclude an earlier ponding by beavers.

The second lake, Llyn Ebyr, is about 600m long by 300m wide, backed to the north and east by the steep wooded slopes of Penycastell, with lower hills to the west. Today it is fringed all around by concealing trees and scrub. It is fed by several small streams and flows out to the southeast via Wigdwr brook, some four kilometres by water down to the Severn. Walking up the brook in mid-summer, the lake was invisible, but sensed by the sound of birds calling across the water, and their splashings as they took off or landed. Peering through the trees, the reed-fringed lake was revealed as an excellent home for beavers, large enough for several families to establish their territories around its shores (Fig. 5.13). They would have had abundant and diverse vegetation to live off, from the deciduous trees on the north-east slopes to willow scrub and marshland plants closer to the water, and reeds and other aquatics within it. The lake is now used by humans for fishing from a boat, the water being quite deep and inhabited by pike and perch.

Fig. 5.13 Llyn Ebyr, seen from its lower end. In the foreground, some slight modern damming by humans, looking not unlike a beaver dam.

Ffigur 5.13 Llyn Ebyr, i'w weld o'i ben isaf. Yn y blaen mae argaeau eithaf modern gan bobl, ond yn edrych yn eithaf tebyg i argae afanc.

The natural basin of Llyn Ebyr's setting, and the current marshy ground beyond the lake, indicate that it could formerly have been larger, as indeed various 19th century travel writings confirm. Samuel Lewis's *Topographical Dictionary of Wales* (first published in 1833, 3rd ed.1845 consulted) gives a brief description of Llyn Ebyr:

' ... about two miles from the town, on the road to Treveglwys, is a spacious pool called Llyn Ebyr, extending over a surface of about fifty acres, and abounding with pike, eels, and perch; it is frequented by wild-fowl, and during the summer is the resort of parties of pleasure, for whose accommodation several boats, belonging to gentlemen in the vicinity, are kept upon the pool.'

(Lewis 1845, vol. ii, 67)

The present, smaller extent of Llyn Ebyr is due partly to natural silting up of the basin, and perhaps also to some lowering of the outflow rim, either deliberately by people or simply through lack of maintenance. When visited, remnants of black polythene sheeting in the woods around the outflow pointed to moderately recent human efforts to reinforce the rim of the lake at this point, to keep up the water level. It is very probable that, like the former Llyn Ffrancon, Llyn Ebyr had its origin in beaver damming of a watercourse, in this case the Wigdwr stream. The creation of the lake may have started early in the post-glacial period with a small dam and pond, that was extended over many, many beaver generations, enabling the lake ecosystem to develop and flourish. Beavers in Canada are known to have created lakes in similar topographical circumstances, and we have seen one in the Algonquin National Park which has endured for several thousand years (Coles and Orme 1983). Likewise, some of the circum-Alpine lakes have in the past been influenced by beaver damming activities that raised or lowered the water level, and some may have been created by beaver damming the first place.

At the end of the field visits to the Moat Lane-Llanidloes lakes, I was in no doubt that Llyn Ebyr was the best candidate as the former *Llyn yr Afangc*. Beavers are likely to have settled in many other local spots from time to time, and along the Severn, but the character of Llyn Ebyr suggests that it was an enduring beaver territory, and one that humans knew and named as such. The name *Llyn yr Afangc* seems all the more appropriate given that the combination of topography and small stream points to beavers having created the lake in the first place.

It was not long after visiting it that I found Llyn Ebyr was in fact identified as the location of the Montgomeryshire *Llyn yr Afangc* in the Melville Richards Archive Place-Name Database. I should have known this all along, having used the database for other sites. I was, however, quite pleased to have independently selected Llyn Ebyr on grounds of its physical character and setting. To have both physical and documentary evidence pointing to the same identification makes it the more certain. However, following up the reference provided in the archive led to new complications.

In the Melville Richards database, the reference provided for Llyn Ebyr being the Montgomeryshire *Llyn yr Afangc* is *The Description of Pembrokeshire*, written by George Owen of Henllys early in the 17th century. This was several decades before Ray and Lhuyd drew attention to the Beaver Pool place-names, and for a time, while I was trying to get hold of a copy of the *Description*, I wondered if they might not have got their inspiration from Owen. Then Nancy Edwards kindly sent me a photocopy of the relevant pages from the *Description*, and she pointed out that the reference occurs in Henry Owen's 1906 edition and consists of the notes referring to p. 147 of another text *A Treatise of Lordshipps Marchers in Wales* by George Owen of Henllys. So it was Henry Owen in the early 20th century who wrote, in a footnote to his editorial notes:

> *'It appears from* Bye-Gones*, New Series, vol.vii (1901-2), p.414 (July 30 1902), that a pool of the Severn about two miles above Llandinam (village) is known by the name [ie* Llyn yr Afangc*]. Bingley (North Wales ed.1804, vol. ii, pp.56-7), speaking of the high ground on the Machynlleth Road "about four miles from Llanidloes", speaks of seeing thence "the woody vales in front with the little Llyn yr Avange (sic),* Beaver's Pool*, at a distance among them". Here he seems to refer to the little lake now called Llyn Ebyr, three miles N.-E. of Llanidloes, which can (the writer believes) be seen from the road at or about the point indicated, and not to any river pool.'*

(Henry Owen 1906, 238-239)

In the 1804 edition of Bingley's *North Wales*, the passage quoted by Owen comes from Chapter 28, 'Machynlleth to Llanydloes', which opens 'The distance from Machynlleth to Llanydloes is about twenty miles, and the road lies over a series of dreary and barren moors.' Bingley walked half the distance before he began to cheer up with a diversion to Frwd y Pennant waterfall (known also as Frwd Fawr), and then comes the relevant passage:

> *'About four miles from Llanydloes, the appearance of the country began to change, and the woody vales in front, with the little Llyn yr Avangc,* Beaver's Pool*, at a distance among them, formed on the whole a pleasing scene.'*

(Bingley 1804, 358)

From the current OS Explorer Map 214, it would appear that when Bingley was four miles from Llanidloes he was looking at a forerunner of the Van reservoir, for although Llyn Ebyr is only a little further off to the east, it is not clearly within sight from the Machynlleth road (B4518) due to the mass of Bryn y Fan. That was a disappointing outcome. However, the modern map turns out to be misleading, for the road network has changed since Bingley's walk. The fold-out map published in the third edition of Bingley's *North Wales* (1839) edited by his son, shows that in the earlier 19th century the road ran to the north and east of Bryn y Fan, and Llyn Ebyr would have been visible to Bingley as he skirted the flanks of the hill (Fig. 5.14). His description of what he saw confirms that the lake now known as Llyn Ebyr was then called Llyn yr Afangc.

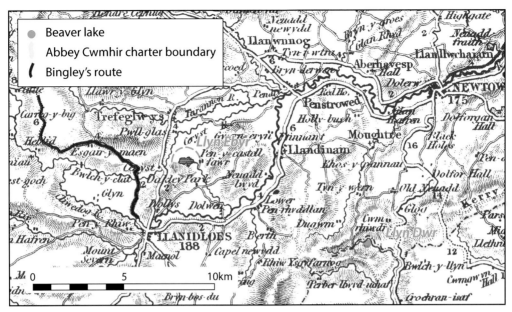

Fig. 5.14 Bingley's map of the Upper Severn area, Llanidloes to Newtown.

Ffigur 5.14 Map Bingley o ran uchaf Afon Hafren, Llanidloes i'r Drenewydd.

Pwll Llostlydan, Radnorshire (Powys)

While working on the location of the Montgomeryshire *Llyn yr Afangc*, my attention was drawn to another possible beaver place-name in mid-Wales. In his research on boundary charters, David Stephenson came across the place-name *pwll llostlydan*, which can be translated as 'pool of the broad-tail', meaning 'pool of the beaver'. Its use in a place-name is unusual. We have seen in Chapter 3 that the name *llostlydan* was used for 'beaver' in the Laws of Hywel Dda, and both Pennant and William Owen Pughe gave *llostlydan* as well as *avancg, avanc* and *azanc* as Welsh names for the beaver. Patrick Neill, writing in the early 19th century about the former presence of beavers in Scotland, mentioned the occurrence of *llosdlydan* in the laws of Hywel Dda (Neill 1819). Others have commented on the similarity of the Welsh *llostlydan* to the Scottish Gaelic *leas-leathen*, in all cases translated as 'broad-tail' and understood to mean 'beaver' (eg. Barrett-Hamilton and Hinton 1921). Aybes and Yalden (1995) noted the *llostlydan* possibility but did not find any examples during their own research on beaver place-names.

Stephenson came across the probable beaver place-name in a charter of Abbey Cwmhir in Radnorshire. In a short paper published in 1970, R. G. Charles provides an account of the charter, which is now in the library of University College London. It records a grant of land made by Roger Mortimer to the abbey in AD 1200, and the bulk of its text sets out the boundaries of the two blocks of land concerned. Following a transcription of the Latin text, Charles suggests the possible course taken by the boundary of the first block, which contains Abbey Cwmhir itself. I have attempted to follow the line on the OS 1:50,000 and 1:25,000 maps, and visited some of the locations, including the stretch where the beaver place-name most probably occurs (see Fig. 5.14).

The Beaver Pool, *Pwll Llostlydan*, occurs along the northernmost stretch of the medieval boundary, which later became the old county boundary between Montgomeryshire and Radnorshire. It comes after the boundary between the parishes of Llandinam and Mochdre meets the county boundary, and before the boundary reaches Camnant Bridge. Along this stretch, about 500m south of the boundary there is a small lake called Llyn Dwr, which can perhaps be translated as 'water hole' (Fig. 5.15). It lies in a shallow marshy basin within the broad rolling hill-tops that stretch to either side of the boundary, backed on the west by the slightly higher Bryn Llyndwr. The ground is drained to the east by a number of small streams that flow to the Camnant. The lake is now about 100m by 80m, and may have covered a larger area in the past, prior to any agricultural improvement. Today's bare, open landscape carries the occasional tree, more than might be appreciated at first sight, including ash, beech, rowan and willow. Their presence indicates the potential for development of willow scrub over the wetter ground, and deciduous tree growth on the drier slopes, thus providing food and building materials for any beavers. It is plausible that Llyn Dwr was once part of a beaver territory and, as with Llyn Ebyr and the former Llyn Ffrancon, it is possible that the lake owes its origin to the effects of beaver dams on one or more of the small streams flowing into a natural hollow or basin.

Fig. 5.15 Llyn Dwr, the possible location of Pwll Llostlydan.

Ffigur 5.15 Llyn Dŵr, lleoliad posib Pwll Llostlydan.

Why *Pwll Llostlydan,* the Beaver Pool, became Llyn Dwr, the Water Lake, is another matter. It may relate to the Pool's importance for watering cattle and other stock on the move. At Llyn Dwr five rights of way converge close to the northwest corner of the lake, two footpaths, one bridleway, one byway and one other track with public access, which together with the name suggests the water was an important resource, attracting travellers from all points of the compass. It may be that this was a watering place for stock that were taken along the Drove Roads such as the Kerry Ridgeway, which starts only four to five kilometres to the east and runs eastwards to Bishop's Castle; there are a number of pools along its route, much needed watering-holes for the cattle that, until the advent of the railways, were driven on the hoof from the Welsh hills to the English Midlands and beyond (one beast might need about fifty litres of water a day, and the average speed of a cattle drove was two miles an hour). Llyn Dwr, understood as 'the watering pool' may have acquired its name after the beavers had gone, and the name 'Pwll Llostlydan' no longer held much meaning for the people using it, but they did need to know where to find plenty of accessible water.

Both Llyn Ebyr and Llyn Dwr are lakes in a basin, with small stream outflows, rather than a pool on a watercourse such as the Conwy *Llyn yr Afangc*. They are close to each other, a little over ten kilometres as the crow flies. Here, as with the Conwy and Nant Ffrancon, there could have been contact between two separate beaver populations, or more probably both were part of a larger group of contiguous territories centred on the Severn. During the field visits to identify the mid-Wales place-name locations, neither Llyn Ebyr nor Llyn Dwr had any fresh bank exposures, and thus no opportunity to search for relic beaver features, but their occurrence to either side of the Severn suggests that it would be worthwhile to undertake a survey along the river in this area.

Another lake with possible beaver connections, recently brought to my attention, is Llangorse, which lies about seven kilometres south of Talgarth on the western side of the Brecon Beacons. The lake is well known for its early medieval crannog, and merits further research. A brief mention should also be made of the place-name Bedd yr Afangc in Pembrokeshire, which I visited some years ago. Bedd yr Afangc is a Neolithic chambered tomb set at the foot of the Preseli Hills; the name can be translated as 'Tomb of the Beaver' or 'Tomb of the Water Monster'. It is likely there were beavers in the vicinity from time to time, but I have not as yet come across any record to suggest a local presence in historic times.

Place-names and beaver features

This chapter has described a first attempt to investigate the Welsh beaver place-names using a combination of documentary sources and field visits to identify and assess the locations in beaver terms, and to search for relic beaver features. The results have confirmed that the places named for beavers are suitable for beaver settlement. Beavers, the ecosystem engineers, are adept at transforming almost any watery place to provide their family with food and security, but the majority of the place-names have turned out to be particularly good in beaver terms.

As a bonus, the field visits have yielded results beyond my initial expectations, in that three of the four beaver-places are not just where beavers once lived, but places where it is likely that beaver activity created the pools in the first place. Two of the three are Llyn Ebyr and Pwll Llostlydan, both 'beaver-pools'. The third is the former Llyn Ffrancon (a modern naming derived from Nant Ffrancon), in the valley that might have been named for its beavers, where beaver dams are commemorated in the name *Sarn yr Afangc*.

The results in terms of identifying relic beaver features along watercourses have also been encouraging, both in the Conwy tributaries and especially in Nant Ffrancon. By focusing the search on rivers with a beaver place-name association, probable dens and burrows and canals have been discovered. What is needed next is to find features that can be dated, and to expand the search beyond the place-name locations. It is likely that features will be found wherever there are suitable river-banks to search, but not in all of them all the time, for just as the features become visible through erosion, so they generally disappear sooner or later because the erosion continues. They are valuable but fragile evidence, and it is important for all likely features to be recorded by whoever finds them, by taking a photo and noting their position, and reporting their discovery. The reporting can be done by contacting the Welsh Beaver Project at *beaver.afanc@wildlifetrustswales.org*

CHAPTER 6

BEAVERS IN WALES: PAST AND FUTURE

In researching the evidence for beavers in Wales I have ventured into areas of scholarship new to me and met new people. I have been helped in many ways, and I have come to know better the beautiful and varied landscapes associated with the beaver evidence. In this chapter, I will try to present an overview, highlighting what I consider to be the more significant aspects of the Welsh beaver story up to the late 19th century, and looking at the possibilities for new discoveries and for a renewed presence of this keystone species in the Welsh fauna. It has become apparent, I hope, that beavers are an integral part of the Welsh natural and cultural environment, albeit one that has been missing for a while. Maybe the telling of their story will encourage their return.

Some thoughts on the character of the evidence

Wales has notably diverse sources of evidence for its beavers, not only the bones and teeth that one might expect. Until recently, however, few people have been familiar with beavers and aware of their former presence, and the evidence has not always been noticed, or recognised for what it is, and its interpretation has been in dispute. Wales is not alone in this respect; the same could be said for most western European countries, even those where small beaver populations survived into the 20th century and have since become the founders of the present resurgence of the species. In addition, while evidence may have been recognised and correctly identified, its significance has not always been fully appreciated, because the extent of beavers' ecological importance for European landscapes is only now beginning to emerge.

The character of the evidence was outlined in Chapter 1. Beaver bones are relatively easy to identify, being robust and chunky, and the incisors are very distinctive. But in parts of Wales, the soils are too acid for bone to survive well, and where it does survive, archaeological funds and expertise have been focused on the identification and analysis of the domestic animals and the larger wild animals, rather than the medium-to-small creatures, again a situation typical of western Europe until recently. Beavers, as we have seen, are actually quite big (medium-large rather than medium-small) and they are economically important animals for humans as well as ecologically important to all, but in their absence they have been perceived as one of the 'small' species of lesser significance, like rabbits and rats maybe. Perhaps now that many more people are becoming interested in and knowledgeable about their local wildlife, and many are members of wildlife and natural history societies, there will be growing pressure for the full range of bone evidence to be identified, dated and analysed. When this happens, there are likely to be a number of surprises, and challenges to prevailing ideas, as with the lynx a few years ago. The species was thought to have become extinct in pre-Roman times but now, thanks to radiocarbon dating of bones from North Yorkshire, we know that lynx survived in Britain at least until the 6th century AD (Hetherington 2006).

Fig. 6.1a Scaup Burn, eroded stream bank where the wood was found.

Ffigur 6.1a Scaup Burn, glan nant wedi erydu lle canfuwyd y pren.

Fig. 6.1b from left to right: Scaup beaver-gnawed branch c.2cm thick; similar modern beaver-gnawed branch; ancient branch c.4cm thick gnawed from two sides; modern branch gnawed from two sides.

Ffigur 6.1b o'r chwith i'r dde: Cangen wedi'i chnoi gan afanc, tua 2cm o drwch; cangen fodern debyg wedi'i chnoi gan afanc; cangen hynafol tua 4cm o drwch wedi'i chnoi o'r ddwy ochr; cangen fodern wedi'i chnoi o'r ddwy ochr.

Once people have handled beaver-gnawed wood, and felt with their finger-tips the characteristic grooves left when beaver incisors cut into wood, and seen both the pencil-point ends of thick beaver-cut branches, and the oblique cut-and-tear on thinner pieces, then they may notice ancient beaver-cut pieces, exposed in a pond freshly dug into former marshland, or in an eroding stream-bank. Recently, at about 300m altitude in the upper reaches of the Tyne catchment near Kielder Water in Northumberland, three bits of wood were noticed in the eroding bank of Scaup Burn (Fig. 6.1a). One piece proved to have been cut by humans, and one had been gnawed by beavers (Fig. 6.1b). The third was a twig, too small to tell who or what broke it from the parent tree. Found in northern England, the wood has wide relevance. It has been radiocarbon dated and found to be at least 400 years more recent than any other radiocarbon-dated physical evidence for beavers throughout Britain, whether beaver bones or beaver-gnawed wood. The radiocarbon date range, late in the 14th century AD, post-dates by two centuries Gerald of Wales' comments on beavers being found only on the Teifi and maybe one river in Scotland. Now we know that beavers were still extant in Britain at least two hundred years later. New finds and more radiocarbon dating may bring the physical record further forward still. The Scaup find is also a reminder that beaver evidence can be found in remote high places as well as in the lowlands, and should encourage anyone walking the Welsh hills to keep their eyes out for similar valuable signs of the former presence of beavers – and of humans too. Like the Yorkshire lynx, one find can significantly alter our understanding of when a species was present in the landscape.

Fig. 6.2 a) Beavers often sit at the water's edge to strip and eat bark from twigs.

Ffigur 6.2 a) Mae afancod yn eistedd ar lan y dŵr yn aml i dynnu a bwyta rhisgl oddi ar frigau.

Photos Mike Symes Devon Wildlife Trust and Duncan Halley NINA.

Lluniau Mike Symes Ymddiriedolaeth Natur Dyfnaint a Duncan Halley NINA.

Fig. 6.2 b) a scatter of peeled twigs is a typical sign of their presence.

Ffigur 6.2 b) mae casgliad o frigau wedi'u pilio yn arwydd o'u presenoldeb.

The debris from beaver feeding is equally distinctive (Fig. 6.2a), and might be found in the organic-rich sediments around a lake shore or along a cut-off stretch of river channel, or some other protected shore-line (Fig. 6.2b). Beavers like to sit at the water's edge when they feed, usually just in the water. They twirl a stick in their front feet, nibbling off the bark, leaving behind a partially or completely de-barked stick that is often patterned with the multiple slanting strokes left by their teeth. Sometimes, the marks are clear enough to distinguish the small teeth of a juvenile from the wider ones of an adult. Normally, a feeding beaver gets through several sticks at a sitting. There may be wood like this preserved in the marshy ground around the fringes of Llyn Ebyr, or eroding out of the Nant Ffrancon sediments as the Ogwen shifts its course. With more people knowing what beaver-gnawed wood looks like, and reporting it when they find it, the evidence base will increase and diversify.

The written evidence relating to beavers extends from the writings of Giraldus in the late 12th century through to the earlier 19th century. The more recent instances refer to the former presence of beavers, rather than beavers alive and well in Wales at the time of writing. The reliability of the written evidence has been considered. The 12th century report by Gerald of Wales, long accepted as accurate in placing beavers on the Teifi in the late 1100s AD, has also been found reliable for the most part in its account of the appearance and habits of beavers. There are nevertheless some misconceptions in Gerald's account. Subsequent authors who add new, accurate information to Gerald's account can be assumed to have had some direct knowledge of beavers, but not certainly from within Wales. Where there is supporting evidence from other sources, such as place-names and relic beaver features, the case for accepting a written report is strengthened. The conjunction of William Owen Pughe's report of beavers on the Ogwen within living memory with the beaver place-names *Sarn yr Afangc* and *Nant Ffrancon* is already promising, and supported by the recent discovery of probable relic beaver features in the eroding banks of the Ogwen as it flows through Nant Ffrancon. It is very likely, I think, that beavers lived here well beyond the medieval period, and maybe into the early-to -mid 18th century. The field surveys carried out in beaver place-name locations have been very important for corroborating written reports and supporting the interpretation of *afangc* place-names as places where beavers once lived.

Other written evidence, such as Buckland's comment that beavers were killed in Wales in the time of Oliver Cromwell, the mid 17th century, is valuable for showing that people were aware that the beaver was a species native to Wales. Buckland's particular comment, while it is not at all specific as to location, does add a little weight to the argument for survival of beavers in Wales for perhaps half a millennium beyond the time of Gerald's report, to within the early years of Edward Lhuyd's explorations in Snowdonia.

There are people who take a more sceptical view of the written evidence than I have done, for example perpetuating Colt Hoare's attitude that the author in question had confused otters with beavers (see Chapter 3, in relation to his translation of Gerald of Wales). Lee

Raye in 2014 published a paper which, he wrote, 'aims to refute the late extinction theory for Britain as a whole'. He does so with vigour, if not always with accuracy, claiming for example that beavers were not classified as vermin in the Act for the Preservation of Grayne. However, as seen in Chapter 4, in the later 16th century Harrison included beavers in his list of vermin covered by the Act: *'I might here intreat largelie of other vermine, as the polcat, the miniuer, the weasell, stote, fulmart, squirrill, fitchew, and such like, which Cardan includeth vnder the word Mustela: also of the otter, and likewise of the beuer, whose hinder feet and taile onlie are supposed to be fish.'* Harrison went on to say quite a bit about beavers, and clearly he saw them as vermin. Some of what he wrote we can now see was fable, but much is accurate, and not merely a repetition of Gerald of Wales' writings. Harrison was the scholar who pondered whether beaver or marten was the more scarce, and I would not follow Raye's example and discard his text, but rather take it as an indication that at the time he was writing, beavers were scarce, like martens.

Raye, in his 2014 paper, compares the records for beavers with those for other native mammals such as otter and badger, which he suggests are 'ecologically similar', and he argues that if beavers were present they should be recorded in roughly similar numbers. I am not convinced as to the similarity of ecological niche, nor of the basic premise that species inhabiting similar niches should occur in similar numbers. The aquatic otters live primarily off other animals, while dryland badgers are omnivores, neither very similar to the semi-aquatic vegetarian beaver. More importantly, Raye does not consider that absence of evidence is not evidence of absence, nor that evidence will not be recognised unless people have the necessary knowledge. The recent find of beaver-gnawed wood on Scaup Burn, mentioned above, is a good example of this. The ecologists prospecting the Scaup area in 2011 realised the wood was unusual, and saved it for further examination. As we have seen, it proved to be beaver-gnawed (Fig. 6.1b), and when it was radiocarbon dated, the result placed the wood in the late 14th century AD (Manning *et al.* 2014). Thus a chance find came to provide evidence of a beaver presence in the Tyne catchment, suggesting that the contemporary tolls imposed on the export of beaver skins could well relate to exploitation of a regional beaver population. This evidence was published in September 2014, just a few months after Raye's paper, so he was not to know of its existence. It does, however, underline how important new sources of evidence can be, and how today's increasing awareness of beavers and their activities may well lead to further support for the written evidence, and help to fill some of the gaps in the current record.

Beaver place-names, neglected in the 20th century, have proved to be one of the most enjoyable and rewarding aspects of the research for this book. This has been in part because several of the locations are so obviously good places for beavers to have lived, which may be partly what led our observant ancestors to give them beaver names. There will still be people who feel that *afangc* is better interpreted as meaning a water-monster rather than a beaver. However, as noted above, the 'water-monster' sense may have evolved in places and at times when local awareness of beavers was in decline, as Blanchet suggested in the mid-20th century for the Rhône valley. He thought the monster known as the Tarasque might have developed from sightings by moonlight of a strange, bulky dark creature emerging onto a river shoal. Edward Lhuyd perhaps had a similar evolution in mind when he commented on local beliefs in monstrous beavers. I have sometimes thought that a family of beavers swimming past in the moonlight might have conjured similar ideas of a monster in someone watching, say, from the shores of Loch Ness.

In addition, place-names have proved a very useful guide for my first attempts at finding relic beaver features. Possible burrows and dens have been recorded in both the Conwy and the Ogwen *afangc* locations, indicating that it would be worthwhile to extend the search into new areas. Ideally, someone will soon find a relic feature associated with beaver-gnawed wood that can be used for radiocarbon dating, or it will be possible to date material from the associated sediments. Then this new category of evidence will not only contribute to our knowledge of the former distribution of beavers in Wales, but also to their occurrence through time. It is unlikely that features will have survived from all the places that beavers once inhabited, but where they do, they will help us to understand more about the history of beavers in Wales and their contributions to habitat evolution. Another new category of evidence, from aDNA analyses, looks to be particularly promising for Wales, with its many lakes and ponds. It could prove to be a most useful tool for identifying beaver presence, and the *afangc* lakes would be a good place to start.

The evidence in space and time

From southeast to northwest, there is evidence for beavers in Wales, from the flat peaty lowlands of Newton Moor and Caldicot to the upper reaches of the Ogwen. They were to be found along the upper Severn, and probably along the Wye, and either side of the border in mid Wales. The physical evidence is not abundant, but it is widespread and of good quality, and in this respect it is similar to other parts of Britain. In fact, there are few regions rich in beaver skeletal remains, apart from the East Anglian Fens. The same is true for wood, although the picture may change with increasing recognition of beaver-gnaw-marks. Elsewhere, there are clusters of place-names, as around Worcester and in Yorkshire. In Scotland, the evidence is widely spread and from varied contexts, similar to Wales but perhaps not as diverse in character. From these distributions, it can be argued that beavers were to be found in all corners of Britain, but not necessarily continuously in all places – just as one expects for their chief predators, wolves and humans.

Chronologically, the first known occurrences of beavers in Britain as a whole are earlier than the first evidence for humans, but in Wales both species are first found in Pontnewydd cave. Given the distribution of mammals across western Europe, it is quite likely that both humans and beavers were present in Wales in earlier times too, but the evidence has either not survived the subsequent glaciations, or not yet been discovered.

Moving on in time, after the last glacial maximum, the first beavers to reach the far northwest of Europe were probably those that spread from the Iberian peninsula and southwestern France through the Atlantic lowlands to Brittany, the Channel River and the Severn-Wye catchment. They spread this far before sea-levels had risen high enough to isolate Britain from the continent, but they were not in the far west soon enough to colonise Ireland, which had probably become an island before the final phases of the last glaciation. Meanwhile, beavers from southeastern Europe were also spreading north and westwards, and across the Doggerland Plains, now under the North Sea, and from there across Britain to the far shores of Cornwall, Wales and Scotland, where the salt sea halted their expansion.

The beaver evidence of prehistoric date from Wales has survived in natural contexts rather than in those created by humans, although there may have been human activity in the same place and at the same time. Even with the arrival of the first farmers, which led to the development of many new cultural contexts such as monuments and burial mounds where evidence might survive, beaver material has yet to be found in such places. What does happen is that, in modern times, archaeologists have excavated ahead of development, or to research the context of a stray find, and in their search for evidence of the lives and activities of earlier humans, they have sometimes come across evidence for beavers as well. Thus, at Caldicot, humans in the past seem to have used the site of a beaver dam for their crossing of the Nedern, and then built a bridge, and they spread beaver-cut wood across muddy ground to make their own trackway. The archaeologists who excavated these structures encountered, recognised and recorded the naturally-occurring beaver evidence in addition to the human evidence that was their main target.

In historic times, it is human intellectual activity that has led to the survival of beaver evidence. People writing down information and ideas, other people making copies of manuscripts, have proved an important source of evidence, especially for the earlier half of the 2nd millennium AD. The advent of printing, and the flourishing state of Welsh scholarship following the stimulus of Renaissance and Reformation, then gave further potential for the recording of information and speculation about beavers. For most of the authors, beavers were a very minor concern, but for anyone researching beavers now, these are valuable sources.

As an aside, the written evidence provides a wealth of variations on the spelling of the Welsh and English words for *Castor fiber*. In English, in the texts used in this book, 'befyr', 'beuer' and 'bever' can be found, in addition to 'beaver'. In Welsh, in addition to 'afanc', there are 'afangc', 'afangk', 'avanc', 'avangk', 'avanke' and 'azanc'. There is also Llostlydan, akin to the Gaelic 'Losleathan' which is interpreted as 'broad-tailed otter' (Coles 2006, 182).

Fig. 6.3 Tympanum over west door of Ribbesford church, beside the Severn, showing a hunter on the left, a dog in the centre and a chunky beaver-like creature on the right.

Ffigur 6.3 Tympanwm uwch ben drws gorllewinol eglwys Ribbesford, ar lan afon Hafren, yn dangos heliwr ar y chwith, ci yn y canol a chreadur mawr tebyg i afanc ar y dde.

The account written by Gerald of Wales at the end of the 12th century provided a strong foundation for human awareness of beavers from then onwards, throughout Britain; it was soundly based on Gerald's own knowledge of beavers, and he had the gift of describing clearly what he had seen. Unsurprisingly, his account includes an element of the fables current in his day, which have their own interest for the light they throw on the ways in which people were using animals to develop and express diverse concepts and ideas, and then to convey them to a wider audience. The story of the beavers castrating themselves is an excellent example of this practice. In England, on the banks of the Severn just downstream of Kidderminster, the church at Ribbesford has a porch over the west door, with a tympanum that portrays the story of a beaver castrating itself to escape the hunters (Fig. 6.3). The elements of hunter and beaver have been distorted to fit the half-circle shape of the carving, leading to the beaver being interpreted as a dragon. The creature, however, is chunky like a beaver, its front feet are raised as a beaver's so often are, it has a broad flat tail, and its back leg is lifted slightly as if to show its (mythical) testicles are missing. Here is a beaver on the way to monsterhood, like its afanc relatives upstream.

From the 16th century onwards, there is a gradual accretion of scraps of reliable information about beavers, from various printed sources. Human society seems always to have kept some small awareness of beavers, and their behaviour, and their presence in Wales, even as the numbers of live beavers dwindled towards extinction. The character of the evidence changes again in the later 19th century, with the extravaganza of Cardiff Castle. Beavers are a minor element of the castle's splendid decorations but, as we have seen, a direct reflection of one man's interest in the species. I have not come across anything to suggest why the young Earl of Bute was interested in beavers, but it is probable that he had read Gerald's *Itinerary* or *Description,* and Pennant's *Tours in Wales.* The live beavers which he imported all went for release in Scotland, not Wales, but the most resplendent memento of their presence is that from Cardiff Castle. And the memento is very much a human cultural reflection of their presence, another way of expressing human interest in the species, to set alongside the writings of Gerald and others.

There are long gaps in the evidence, notably during the earlier prehistoric period. It is possible that there were no beavers in Wales during the blank millennia, but more likely that they were present but no evidence has yet been recognised and reported. In Britain as a whole there are some suggestions of an ebb and flow of beaver presence, with a decline in evidence during the period of Roman occupation, followed by a marked increase from about AD 600. Some of the fluctuation can be explained by changing human habits, for example heavy hunting during the later Iron Age, possibly for export of furs to the Romanised world, may have caused a decline in numbers. A few centuries later, when people began to include beaver incisors in some of their burials, as the Anglo-Saxons did in England, the amount of beaver evidence recovered by archaeologists increases. In Wales, it is the development of a written record that brings beavers securely back into view by the later 12th century, through the developed Laws of Hywel Dda and the writings of Gerald of Wales. The nature of what Gerald wrote is particularly important, for he specifies exactly where the beavers were living, on a particular stretch of a particular river, the Teifi at Cilgerran, and when – the 1180s. He leaves no doubt of there being a beaver population in Wales at this time, which is partly what has encouraged me to pursue the faint traces of their presence in the centuries immediately before and following.

It is very difficult to pinpoint the extinction of a species, and it is no easier to say when beavers became extinct in Wales than it is for Britain as a whole. It has often been assumed that, because Gerald of Wales wrote that they were to be found only on the Teifi, they were scarce in England and Wales in his time and became extinct soon after, by the end of the 13th century if not before. However, as we have seen above, dating the piece of wood from Scaup Burn in Northumberland has demonstrated this was not the case. Other species, like the lynx mentioned above, have been found to have survived for much longer than generally thought, and it is possible for a shrinking population to stabilise and survive in low numbers for a long while. This seems to have been the case for mammoths in Eurasia, which survived well beyond the end of the last glaciations. Their range, and therefore probably the size of their population, had shrunk greatly during the course of the last glaciations, and for Britain the most recent evidence comes from the end of the glacial period, from Condover in Shropshire, where the bones of four or five mammoths were found in a former kettle-hole. But in the far northeast of the Eurasian landmass, they survived until about six thousand years ago, and on Wrangel Island, which lies off the

Siberian coast, the most recent mammoth remains have been dated to about four thousand years ago, 2000 BC, about the time that the people of Wales first began to use metals.

Fig. 6.4 Nant Ffrancon, looking upstream from Ceunant. *Photo John Coles.*

Ffigur 6.4 Nant Ffrancon, wrth edrych i fyny'r afon o Geunant. *Llun John Coles.*

After Gerald of Wales, none of the scholars who wrote about beavers appear to have seen them for themselves, except perhaps for Edward Lhuyd in North Wales, and Thomas Pennant during his travels on the continent. They do, however, have some knowledge of beavers beyond what they might have learned from reading Gerald's accounts. This might have come from discussion with people in Wales or other parts of Britain, people who perhaps still had a small local beaver population. When Edward Lhuyd, in the 1690s, wrote that the vulgar people did not know what a beaver was, he implied that there were people who did know, himself included. As mentioned above, beavers can live largely hidden from human view, sometimes in remote upland valleys, and maybe more often under people's noses on a deep river or some other large body of water. Without dams, lodges and recently-felled trees, the nocturnal semi-aquatic beavers may not be spotted by the diurnal land-based humans. It is interesting that the information relayed by William Owen Pughe in the 1790s, that there had been beavers living in Nant Ffrancon in living memory, comes from a valley where beavers probably would have dammed the watercourse in places, and where the place-name *Sarn yr Afangc* indicates that humans knew of the dams, and knew who had built them (Fig. 6.4). Possibly the beavers had died out by 1650, but maybe they were still in the valley in the early 18th century, and they may even have been there as late as 1740-1760.

Fig. 6.5 One of the beavers adorning the Library bookcases at Cardiff castle, a memento of the brief 19th century re-introduction of beavers to Wales.

Ffigur 6.5 Un o'r afancod sy'n addurno silffoedd llyfrau'r llyfrgell yng Nghastell Caerdydd, sy'n ein hatgoffa am ailgyflwyno afancod i Gymru am gyfnod byr yn y 19eg ganrif.

Whether beavers were extinct in Wales by the late 18th century, as Thomas Pennant believed, is another matter. He was an experienced and respected observer of natural history, and he knew what a beaver looked like, for he described and illustrated them in his own work. On balance, I would suggest he was right, but it is just possible that they survived for a while longer on some deep river, or along a remote upland stream, where few people noticed them and those who did failed, for one reason or another, to comment on their existence. Perhaps the only proof of such late survival will come, not from written records, but from the discovery and dating of a piece of gnawed wood or a relic beaver feature. My own view is that this will probably happen, as more people recognise beaver evidence for what it is, and the record expands in space and time. Perhaps beavers will be found to have survived into the early 18th century, or a few decades longer.

While it is not possible to prove exactly when it was that beavers became extinct in Wales, what I have found is a continuous thread of human awareness of beavers. From the first written records onwards they are perceived as a species native to Wales, and moreover a species with a cultural relevance expressed in law and literature and oral tradition. Edward Lhuyd drew the cultural threads together with his interest in language and history, exemplified in his study of *afangc* place-names, as shown in his work for Gough's edition of Camden's *Britannia*. Through the centuries there was also a gradual accretion of understanding of beaver behaviour, culminating in Pennant's inclusion of beavers in *British Zoology*. The Marquis of Bute's pioneering re-introduction then provides a neat late 19th century stepping stone to the current situation (Fig. 6.5).

CHAPTER 7

RETURN AND RESTORATION

Return of the Beavers

In recent decades, there has been much talk of reintroducing beavers to Britain, and also some action. Under the European Commission's Habitats Directive, member countries are expected to reintroduce former native species which are currently extinct within their own boundaries, providing that suitable conditions exist. To take an extreme example of a species that is not currently under consideration, long ago during a warm interglacial period, the hippopotamus was native to southern Britain, but due to climate change and to human cultural development and expansion, it would not now find appropriate conditions, and should not be reintroduced. Several bird species have been successfully re-introduced since the mid-20th century and others have arrived under their own steam. One species which has recently established itself, with some help from humans, is the crane. In 2017 cranes successfully raised young on both sides of the Severn estuary, the ones on the Welsh side close to the Goldcliff archaeological site where Martin Bell has found crane footprints, alongside those of other species, dating to the Mesolithic (Bell pers. com.). Beavers, which are one of the most adaptable of mammalian species, would find a suitable climate and plenty of good habitat in Britain, and the process of their return is at different stages in Scotland, England and Wales.

Fig. 7.1 a) A beaver dam in Knapdale, south-west Scotland, built by beavers released for the Scottish Beaver Trial. b) The humans on the dam give an idea of its size and strength. Photos taken in 2012.

Ffigur 7.1 a) Argae afanc yn Knapdale, de orllewin yr Alban, a adeiladwyd gan afancod a ryddhawyd ar gyfer Arbrawf Afancod yr Alban. b) Mae'r bobl ar yr argae'n rhoi syniad o'i faint a'i gryfder. Tynnwyd y lluniau yn 2012.

In May 2008, after much discussion and controversy, the Scottish government granted a licence for a trial release of beavers into the wild. A small number of beavers from mainland Europe were brought in to Britain, and kept in quarantine for six months. In May 2009 the trial began, with the release of several beavers in south-west Scotland, in Knapdale Forest, Ayrshire, and further beavers were released there in 2010. The project was a joint undertaking by the Royal Zoological Society of Scotland, the Scottish Wildlife Trust and Forestry Commission Scotland, with independent scientific monitoring co-ordinated by Scottish Natural Heritage. Within a year or so, the beaver families had established their separate territories, with dams and lodges as necessary (Fig. 7.1), and they had begun to breed, with young first sighted in 2010. The trial ran for five years, to give time for various aspects of beaver activity to be monitored and assessed, and a detailed report was presented to the Scottish government. In November 2017, the Scottish Government announced that beavers would be given protected status in Scotland, and it is to be hoped that this will soon be finalised.

In fact, there were beavers in the wild a little earlier than expected. Late in 2010, beavers on the other side of Scotland came to public attention, with press reports of beavers living wild along the Tay. It appears that slight indications of beavers had been noticed for several years. A few of these were due to known escapes of beavers from nearby private enclosures, and the beavers were trapped and returned to an enclosure (not necessarily the one they had escaped from). However, it seems that some remained free, and several beaver families had become established in the Tay catchment. Now the population has grown, and there are beavers settled in a diversity of habitats within the Tay catchment.

In England there has been a growing number of large enclosures with beavers, often brought in to improve the state of a wetland reserve. In 2001, Kent Wildlife Trust was one of the first to use beavers as managers of a wetland nature reserve, followed subsequently by the Wildfowl and Wetlands Trust at their reserves at Martin Mere and at Slimbridge. The Cotswold Water Park has had beavers since 2005, and three beaver enclosures have been established in Devon, at Escot, Broadwoodwidger and Boldventure. The Boldventure beavers are important participants in a Devon Wildlife Trust research project that began in 2011, to improve the management of Culm Grassland. Meanwhile, in 2008 a report on *The Feasibility and acceptability of reintroducing the European beaver to England* was produced for Natural England and the Peoples Trust for Endangered Species, since when there have been a number of developments.

A couple of years after the Boldventure enclosure was set up, over in east Devon beavers were found to be living wild on the river Otter. Although Defra decreed that the beavers should be captured and removed, there was strong local and national support for them to remain. The Devon Wildlife Trust, with first-hand knowledge of beavers gained from their Boldventure project, put forward a case for a five year trial, which Defra accepted and in 2015, after identity and health checks, the beavers were released back into the river (Fig. 7.2). By 2017 there were beavers settled along the tributaries to the Otter as well as the main river. Some of the families have built dams, and by 2018 around eight territories had been established. Meanwhile, the Cornwall Wildlife Trust established its own beaver project, releasing a pair into a large enclosure in the summer of 2017. They have about two hectares of wooded land, and a stream, which they soon began to dam. Both these south-western projects are being monitored by the University of Exeter.

Fig. 7.2 In 2015, beavers found living wild on the River Otter were trapped, given a health and identity check and then released, to be monitored as part of the Devon Wildlife Trust's Beaver Project. *Photo Nick Upton Naturepl.com/Devon Wildlife Trust.*

Ffigur 7.2 Yn 2015, cafodd afancod a ganfuwyd yn byw'n wyllt ar Afon Otter eu dal, cawsant eu harchwilio o ran iechyd a beth oeddent ac wedyn eu rhyddhau, i'w monitro fel rhan o Brosiect Afancod Ymddiriedolaeth Natur Dyfnaint. *Llun Nick Upton Naturepl.com/Ymddiriedolaeth Natur Dyfnaint.*

Most recently, and closest to Wales, in late 2017 Natural England approved a plan to release beavers in a large enclosure (6.5 hectares) in the Forest of Dean, partly in the hope that the beavers would dam the stream running through the enclosure, thereby lessening the flood risk downstream. The enclosure was prepared in the early months of 2018, and in July the first pair were released. The stream that runs through the enclosure is in the upper eastern reaches of the Wye catchment.

In Wales, the Welsh Beaver Project was established in 2005 to investigate the possibilities and difficulties of reintroduction. An ecological feasibility report was published in 2009, and a full report, which also included an assessment of beaver management issues and the desirability of a beaver reintroduction, was produced in 2012. Various proposals have since been made for a reintroduction, but as yet none have been approved, partly due

Avanke, Bever, Castor

to changes of direction within Natural Resources Wales, a body newly formed in 2012 by the amalgamation of the three main government agencies concerned with the natural environment. Currently (2018), the Welsh Beaver Project, led by the Wildlife Trusts in Wales, is working to identify suitable sites for a reintroduction, and preparing for a licence application to reintroduce beavers to the wild (Leow-Dyke pers. com.). Meanwhile, in late 2011, the Blaeninion conservation project released two beavers in an enclosure near Machynlleth in west Wales. To the south-west in Carmarthenshire, the Bevis Trust established one beaver family in an enclosure on their land in 2014, and the Trust has subsequently built and populated a further two enclosures. To the east, close to Llangors, beavers were introduced to an enclosure on the Eligro nature reserve in 2013 (Fig. 7.3).

Fig. 7.3 A female beaver living in the Eligro Nature Reserve near Llangors. There have been beavers breeding here since 2013. *Photo Alicia Leow-Dyke, Welsh Beaver Project.*

Ffigur 7.3 Afanc benywaidd yn byw yng Ngwarchodfa Natur Eligro ger Llangors. Mae afancod wedi bod yn magu yma ers 2013. *Llun Alicia Leow-Dyke, Prosiect Afancod Cymru.*

Enclosures have proved valuable for research on beavers, and for familiarising humans with beavers and their activities but, however big, they are not representative of the full range of the long-term effects of the species, mainly because the enclosure unnaturally concentrates their activity, and inhibits the natural extent and evolution of a territory. Scotland and England have beavers living wild, and perhaps these will help to provide the information needed to initiate a Welsh wild beaver trial – after all, river catchments often ignore humanly-devised boundaries, and beavers are not conscious of political borders.

Restoration of the Landscape

Why would I want to encourage the return of beavers to Wales? Not just because they are a native species, which the Habitats Directive suggests should be brought back if at all possible, but mainly because of their vital contribution to the restoration of a more natural ecosystem, a 'rewilding' in current terminology. The wildlife of Britain as a whole has taken a hammering as the human population has risen alongside developments in human means of exploiting the land. There has been, for several millennia, an expansion and intensification of farming, replacing wild vegetation with cultivated crops and pasture for domestic animals, thereby altering the former ecosystems. Change is natural, and species adapt but, seen over the long term, a tipping point will be reached after which some communities cannot recover or adapt naturally. Moreover, as time has passed, the human population has grown and human society has become more complex, and the deliberate human manipulation of wild populations has increased. Roger Lovegrove, in *Silent Fields* (2007) charts the culling of wildlife in Britain. He explores the impact of the Tudor Vermin Acts, discussed above, which from the earlier 16th century onwards determined which species were 'vermin', and the Acts encouraged their extermination by paying bounty on their heads. The persecution continued with the introduction of Game Laws from the later 17th century onwards, protecting game species at the expense of their competitors and predators. Lovegrove notes that in 17th century Wales, almost 5000 bounty payments were made for the heads of wild cats, and in the last quarter of the 19th century, the vermin killed on one Welsh estate included nearly 5000 weasels and 3000 stoats, alongside almost 2000 kestrels and 1500 carrion crows, with lesser numbers of another ten species.

Occasionally there were individuals who saw the world differently. One such is portrayed by Julia Blackburn in her 1989 biography of Charles Waterton. A Yorkshire land owner, a naturalist, and something of an eccentric, Waterton travelled in South America as a young man, and returned home in 1813 to turn his land into a protected oasis for wild animals. He did this prompted by the contrast between the abundant wildlife of South America and the impoverished situation at home, and his method was to build a huge stone wall around his estate. Many others have had similar concerns in subsequent decades, sometimes focussed on plants, sometimes animals, sometimes landscapes, leading to the rise of conservation organisations such as the National Trust, Royal Society for the Protection of Birds, and the Wildlife Trusts, all with strong memberships. Over time, the aims of conservation bodies have evolved in the light of the progress or otherwise of the projects they have undertaken. Over time, too, there have been shifts in public opinion, in funding and in legislation.

In the last decade, one of the approaches to conservation which has come to the fore is that of rewilding. One of rewilding's most active exponents is George Monbiot, an environmental journalist resident in Wales, and author of a number of books. In *Feral* (2013) Monbiot points out that 'rewilding'is a relatively new word, which means different things to different people. For him, it means allowing change to take place naturally and, by implication, at landscape rather than enclosure scale. This he contrasts with the approach to conservation which aims to keep an ecosystem 'in a state of arrested development' (2013, p.9). 'Rewilding', he stresses, 'unlike conservation, has no fixed objective; it is driven not by human management but by natural processes' (2013, p.83), and for him one of the natural agents of change is the beaver. In England, a rewilding project that might have Waterton's Wall somewhere in its ancestry is underway in Sussex, without beavers as yet but with a number of large herbivores and browsers. This, the rewilding of the 3,500 acre Knepp estate, began around 2000, and progress to date has been chronicled by Isabella Tree in *Wilding* (2018). Her book is also a useful guide to the development of rewilding in western Europe. There are problems with some aspects of these projects, but the humans guiding them are learning to adapt to local circumstances. The Bevis Trust and Blaeninion beaver restoration projects, mentioned above, have similar aims of rewilding. It is against this background that the relevance of beavers becomes obvious, as natural agents of change.

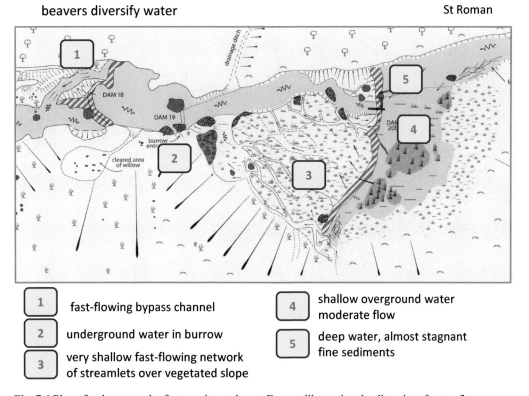

beavers diversify water   St Roman

1 fast-flowing bypass channel	**4** shallow overground water moderate flow
2 underground water in burrow	**5** deep water, almost stagnant fine sediments
3 very shallow fast-flowing network of streamlets over vegetated slope	

Fig. 7.4 Plan of a short stretch of stream in south-east France, illustrating the diversity of water flow created by three beaver dams.

Ffigur 7.4 Cynllun o ddarn byr o afon yn ne ddwyrain Ffrainc, yn dangos amrywiaeth llif y dŵr wedi'i greu gan dri argae gan afancod.

Beavers, in ecological terms, are a keystone species. They slot into place and hold up the structure, providing the conditions for other species, both plant and animal, to flourish. Their presence enhances conditions for wildlife at every level, from micro-organisms in the water to land mammals drinking from the bank and humans enjoying a twilight beaver watch from a canoe. Some of the more significant changes following beaver settlement along a stream come about where they build dams and create ponds (Fig. 7.4), but changes can happen wherever beavers graze and browse and diversify the flow of water. They induce an increase in biomass, due to the dams holding back water and sediments, and in effect acting as a nutrient trap (Fig. 7.5). Plant life is abundant, thanks to water and nutrients and light, from aquatics in the pond to the climbers that grow through the mix of old and new tree growth. There is more food for insects and amphibians and fish, and the whole food chain benefits, from primary grazers to the predators at the top, whether it be the swallows that catch insects in flight, the woodpeckers that drill them out of the standing dead trees, or the pike that catch waterfowl chicks as they paddle across the pond. Otters may come to catch fish and frogs, and to rest up in a beaver lodge along with the water voles that have been grazing on the marshland vegetation around the pond. Humans may turn up, also to fish, using beaver wood to light a fire and cook their catch. Overall, there is more vegetation and more animal life, in greater diversity, thanks to the beavers' presence.

Fig 7.5a and b Two dams downstream of Fig. 4, flowing through rough pasture and walnut orchards in south-east France. Before the arrival of beavers, there were no ponds in the area apart from one small domestic reservoir. Now, with about thirty dams along a 900m stretch of the stream, there is a much greater abundance of water in diverse contexts along the stream line, providing habitat for a marked increase in plant and animal species.

Ffigurau 7.5a a b Dau argae i lawr yr afon o Ffigur 4, yn llifo drwy borfa fras a pherllannau cnau Ffrengig yn ne ddwyrain Ffrainc. Cyn dyfodiad yr afancod, nid oedd unrhyw byllau yn yr ardal, ar wahân i un gronfa ddŵr fechan ddomestig. Nawr, gydag oddeutu 30 o argaeau ar hyd darn 900m o'r nant, mae llawer mwy o ddŵr mewn cyd-destunau amrywiol ar hyd y nant, yn darparu cynefin ar gyfer cynnydd nodedig mewn rhywogaethau o blanhigion ac anifeiliaid.

With growing evidence of climate change and its consequences, another basic effect of beaver presence may become increasingly relevant to our human society. Beaver territories retain more water than similar areas without beavers. This comes about in several ways – a widening of the water course, the creation of ponds, water led into river banks underground along beaver burrows and at the surface along beaver canals. These changes contribute to the diversification of water flow and to a local increase in water volume which, together with any water held in ponds, raises the local water table (Westbrook, Cooper and Butler 2013). As a result, after heavy rain there may be less flooding downstream than before the beavers established their territory. This comes about because the water moves more slowly through the area of the territory than it did before. One North American study, based on computer modelling of water flow through an area of about 2.5 km² (one square mile), has produced some interesting figures (Müller-Schwarze and Sun 2003, 166). If there were no beaver dams, water would flow through the area in three to four hours. If there was one leaky beaver dam about 1.5m high, the same water would take eleven days to flow through, and if the dam was well-maintained it would take up to nineteen days. A well-established beaver territory on a stream might have four to six well-maintained dams which, based on this modelling, would dramatically slow the flow of water. In fact, this is very much what is happening in the Boldventure enclosure in Devon, according to the monitoring results which show that the beaver dams slow down the passage of water in times of flood by storing it in the ponds, whereas in times of drought more water is released (Elliott *et al.* 2017).

Fig. 7.6 On the left, the river Bes, too wide for beavers to dam. Flowing through a mix of woodland, scrub and arable land, it is thick with silt following a period of heavy rainfall. Coming in from the right, a small tributary colonised by a beaver family which has built at least eight dams upstream; the water is silt-free as it joins the river.

Ffigur 7.6 Ar y chwith, afon Bes, sy'n rhy llydan i afancod godi argae arni. Yn llifo drwy gymysgedd o goetir, llwyni a thir âr, mae'n drwchus gyda llifwaddod yn dilyn cyfnod o lawiad trwm. Yn dod i mewn o'r dde mae llednant fechan lle mae teulu o afancod yn byw ac maent wedi adeiladu o leiaf 8 argae i fyny'r afon; nid oes llifwaddod yn y dŵr fel mae'n ymuno â'r afon.

During fieldwork in the Drôme in southeastern France and in Brittany, it often rained heavily and for a long time, and we had many opportunities to see the effects of beaver dams on water flow, confirming that in real life, as well as in computer modelling and in enclosures, the dams hold back rain water and lessen the likelihood of flooding downstream. We noted too that much of the sediment from rain-driven soil erosion of the surrounding land was held in the beaver ponds. In one instance, when we were mapping a territory that straddled the confluence of a small stream and a river, we found the river flowing brown and silty following heavy rain, but the small stream flowed in clear (Fig. 7.6). The river was too wide and fast flowing to have any beaver dams. The stream had four or five maintained dams, and these trapped the soil washed in by the rain from the surrounding fields.

Experiments with beaver engineering have been going on for some time. One environmental restoration project carried out in Wyoming in the late 1970s was based on this potential for beaver activity to retain water and sediments within a territory. In one very degraded catchment, beavers (*Castor canadensis*) and the human environmental managers together built dams which raised the local water table by up to a metre. This in turn encouraged willow growth, which helped to stabilise the ground. The dams also trapped the soil washed in from surrounding land, and the ponds retained up to 90% of the sediment load that was carried downstream prior to damming. The pond sediments in turn trapped nitrogen and phosphorus, all of which encouraged further plant growth, and at the same time cleaned up the water before it flowed on downstream. The humans' main input to the project was to provide the beavers with high quality dam-building materials in the early stages, and to reinforce some dams with chicken wire and old tyres, as the area was so degraded to begin with that the beavers had no wood to build with and their dams tended to wash out after heavy rain. The project cost $4000 for materials plus the wages of the human managers (in the 1970s, maybe equivalent to about £3000 at the time), and it was estimated that a team of human water engineers would have charged at least $100,000 (c.£75,000) to achieve the same effects (Müller-Schwarze and Sun 2003, 167-168). Similar figures for the retention of sediments behind beaver dams have been recorded in *Castor fiber* territories, for example in Russia to the south east of Moscow, three dams along one small river trapped over 4000 tonnes of sediment in one recent flooding episode (Gorshkov, D., in Sjöberg and Ball (eds) 2013).

As well as flooding, our world seems to be at increased risk of drought, as climate change pushes weather systems to extremes. Here too the beaver territories which retain water can make a significant beneficial contribution. It is immediately obvious that aquatic and semi-aquatic plants and animals are more likely to survive a drought if beaver activity has retained water in a territory, than if there were no beavers and no such activity. The benefits would be felt throughout a catchment, as dams in the upper reaches slowly released water to give a low but prolonged flow rather than a speedy transit to the sea.

During the Beaver Works Project, we recorded some of the effects of beavers on water retention, such as the number of ponds in a territory and their size, and the width of the stream channel within the territory compared to that above and below. We found that on one low-gradient stream, in a beaver territory about 900m long, with six active dams, there was a minimum six-fold increase in water volume. On a steeper stream, due to local conditions we only recorded the relevant information for a short stretch of 90m with three active dams, and here we estimated a thirty-five-fold increase in water volume compared to the probable volume before the beavers arrived (Fig. 7.7). These estimates are no more than a guide, but enough to show that beavers could play a very important role in mitigating the effects of drought as well as those of floods.

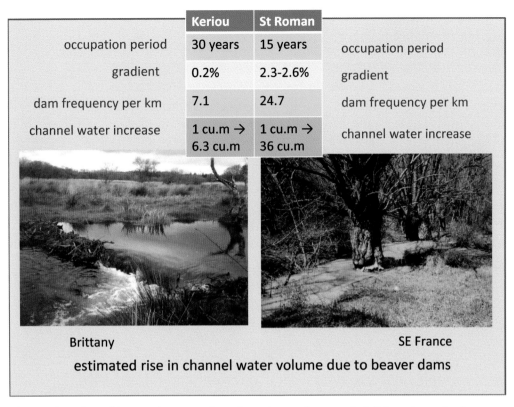

	Keriou	St Roman	
occupation period	30 years	15 years	occupation period
gradient	0.2%	2.3-2.6%	gradient
dam frequency per km	7.1	24.7	dam frequency per km
channel water increase	1 cu.m → 6.3 cu.m	1 cu.m → 36 cu.m	channel water increase

Brittany   SE France

estimated rise in channel water volume due to beaver dams

Fig. 7.7 The estimated increase in water volume due to beaver dams; on the left for a stream flowing through flat landscape in Brittany (see Fig. 1.3) ; on the right for the stream shown in Figs 7.4 and 7.5, flowing through hilly country.

Ffigur 7.7 Y cynnydd a amcangyfrifir mewn dwysedd dŵr oherwydd argaeau afancod; ar y chwith ar gyfer nant yn llifo drwy dirwedd wastad yn Llydaw (gweler Ffigur 1.3); ar y dde ar gyfer y nant a ddangosir yn Ffigurau 7.4 a 7.5, yn llifo drwy wlad fryniog.

On the European mainland, there are now beavers in almost every country where they were formerly to be found. This has happened either through natural expansion, as with their spread up the Rhône valley in France, or with the help of humans who have trapped beavers in areas of plenty for release in regions without beavers. Beavers released in southern Germany are now widespread, and their offspring have provided a breeding nucleus for new populations elsewhere. Management of the beavers in Bavaria is particularly well-developed, with a network of local beaver wardens, and well-tested solutions for any problems caused by beaver activity, such as flooding of a road or arable land. In Denmark, eighteen beavers were released in the Klosterheden State Forest in 1999; the forest consists of heathland, farmland and conifer plantations and by 2009 when I visited the area, there were numerous dams and ponds along the streams, with increasing variety of plant and animal life (Fig.7.8). The release of beavers in Netherlands has a particular interest, since human engineering in that country ensures very close control of water levels, and one might have expected that beaver water engineers would not be welcome, but this is not at all the case. The first beavers were released in the late 1980s, since when further small groups have been released in a variety of other areas. Many of the beavers are serving as nature reserve managers, including some of those living close to areas of dense human habitation, farming and industry. There seems to have been very little conflict of interest between the beavers and the humans, and no call for the beavers to be removed. On the contrary, the beavers are seen as an asset to the Netherlands, valuable restorers of wetland ecosystems and a boost to wildlife in general. Humans also benefit from the rewilding, from eco-tourism, from the educational opportunities, and from the sheer enjoyment of exploring a beaver territory.

Figure 7.8 Klosterheden beaver dam, with a lodge near the tree, both built predominately of bog myrtle. This is one of the many ponds that diversify local wildlife, and because it is close to a road, a pipe has been stuck through the dam (by humans) to keep the water level just below that of the road.

Ffigur 7.8 Argae afanc Klosterheden, gyda gwâl ger y goeden, wedi'i greu'n bennaf o helyg Mair. Dyma un o'r pyllau niferus sy'n creu amrywiaeth o fywyd gwyllt lleol, a chan ei fod yn agos at ffordd, mae pibell wedi cael ei rhoi drwy'r argae (gan bobl) i gadw lefel y dŵr yn is na lefel y ffordd.

Wales too should see the return of this keystone species to the wild, beavers bringing with them the restoration of a rich natural environment, increasing biodiversity and contributing to water management and water quality. They will provide a starting point for the environmental understanding and entertainment of the humans who live alongside them, or who come from further afield to see them. Maybe, in due course, there will be new stories of the *afanc*, spotted by moonlight on the lake shores and in the rivers and streams of Wales.

REFERENCES

Aldhouse-Green, S. Peterson, R. and Walker, E.A. 2012 *Neanderthals in Wales. Pontnewydd and the Elwy Valley Caves.* Oxford and Oakville, Oxbow Books.

Aybes, C. and Yalden, D. 1995 Place-name evidence for the former distribution and status of Wolves and Beavers in Britain. *Mammal Review* 25, 201-227.

Barrett-Hamilton, G.E.H. and Hinton, M.A.C. 1921 *A History of British Mammals.* London, Gurney and Jackson.

Bartholomew, J G. (ed.) 1914 *The Survey Gazeteer of the British Isles.* Edinburgh, John Bartholomew & Co.

Bingley, W. 1804 *North Wales.* London, Longman and Rees.

Bingley, W.R. 1839 *Excursions in North Wales* (an updated edition edited by W. Bingley's son). London, Longman, Orme and Co.

Blackburn, Julia 1989 *Charles Waterton, Traveller and Conservationist.* London, The Bodley Head.

Blanchet, M. 1994 *Le castor et son royaume.* Lausanne, Delachaux et Niestlé. (2nd edition; 1st edition published 1977).

Brown, A.G., Basell, L. and Farbstein, R. 2017 Eels, Beavers and Horses: Human Niche Construction in the European Late Upper Palaeolithic. *Proceedings of the Prehistoric Society* 83, 1-22.

Buckland, F. 1863 *Curiosities of Natural History.* 7th edition. London, Bentley.

Buckland, F. 1887 *Notes and Jottings from Animal Life.* London, Smith Elder.

Buffon, Comte de 1760 *Histoire Naturelle.* Paris, L'Imprimerie Royale.

Bye-gones 1901-02 New Series vol.vii (1901-2).

Camden, W. 1586 *Britannia.* London, R. Newbery.

Campbell-Palmer, R., Gow, D., Needham, R., Jones, S. and Rosell, F. 2015 *The Eurasian Beaver.* Exeter, Pelagic Publishing.

Coles, B. 2006 *Beavers in Britain's Past.* Oxford, Oxbow Books.

Coles, B. 2010 The European Beaver. In O'Connor, T. and Sykes, N. (eds) *Extinctions and Invasions. A Social History of British Fauna,* 104-115. Oxford, Windgather Press.

Coles, B. 2012 Beavers at Pontnewydd. In Aldhouse-Green, S. Peterson, R. and Walker, E.A. 2012 *Neanderthals in Wales. Pontnewydd and the Elwy Valley Caves,* 104-107. Oxford and Oakville, Oxbow Books.

Coles, J.M. and Orme, B. J. 1983 *Homo sapiens* or *Castor fiber*? *Antiquity* 57, 95-102.

Conroy, J.W.H., Kitchener, A.C. and Gibson, J A. 1998 The History of the Beaver in Scotland and its Future Reintroduction. In R.A. Lambert (ed.) *Species History in Scotland*, 107-128. Edinburgh, Scottish Cultural Press.

Crone, A., Cavers, G., Davies, K., Mackay, H., and Whitehouse, N. In press. Nasty, Brutish and Short? The Lifecycle of an Iron Age Roundhouse. *Journal of Wetland Archaeology.*

Dent, A. 1974 *Lost Beasts of Britain.* London, Harrap.

Elliott, M., Blythe, C., Brazier, R.E., Burgess, P., King, S., Puttock, A., Turner, C. 2017 *Beavers – Nature's Water Engineers.* Devon Wildlife Trust.

Érome, G. 1982 *Contribution à la connaissance* éco-éthologique *du castor (*Castor fiber*) dans la vallée du Rhône.* PhD thesis, Université Claude Bernard – Lyon 1.

Ewen, A.H. and Prime, C.T. 1975 *Ray's Flora of Cambridgeshire.* Hitchen, Wheldon and Wesley.

Fernandez, C-E. 2012 *Legends of the lakes of Wales: thematic classification and analysis.* Dissertation, MA in Celtic Studies, available at: repository.uwtsd.ac.uk

Furnivall, F.J. (ed.) 1868 *Manners and Meals in Olden Time. The Babees Book. The Bokes of Nurture. Etc.* Early English Text Society Original Series 32. London, Trüber and Co., reprinted 1990 by Kraus Reprint, Millwood, N.Y.

Green, H.S. 1984 *Pontnewydd Cave: a lower Palaeolithic hominid site in Wales: the first report.* Cardiff, National Museum of Wales.

Gibson, E. (ed.) 1695 *Camden's Britannia* (first English edition).

Gilmour, J. 1944 *British Botanists.* London, William Collins.

Gough, R. (ed.) 1789 *Britannia, by William Camden.* London, J. Nichols.

Harrison, W. 1586 *The Description of England. Holinshed's Chronicles of England, Scotland and Ireland.* Vol. 1(3). Reprinted 1807. London, J. Johnson *et al.*

Hibbert, F.A. and Switsur, V.R. 1976 Radiocarbon dating of Flandrian pollen zones in Wales and northern England. *New Phytologist* 77, 793-807.

Hoare, Sir Richard Colt. 1806 *Itinerary of Archbishop Baldwin through Wales, A. D. MCLXXXVIII.* By Giraldus de Barri; tr. into English, and illustrated with views, annotations, and a life of Giraldus, by Sir Richard Colt Hoare, bart. ... London, William Miller.

Hubback, David. 1987 *Time and the Valley. The Past, Present and Future of the Upper Ogwen Valley.* LLanrwst, Gwasg Carreg Gwalch.

Huws, Daniel 1989 *Peniarth 28: illustrations from a Welsh Lawbook.* (Aberystwyth: The National Library of Wales, 1989) *www.llgc.org.uk*

Johnston, Dafydd 2004 'Lewys Glyn Cothi (*fl.* 1447–1489)', *Oxford Dictionary of National Biography*, Oxford University Press, 2004 [*http://0-www.oxforddnb.com.lib.exeter.ac.uk/view/article/16571*, accessed 22 Aug 2011]

Jones, Brinley R. 2007 'Llwyd, Humphrey (1527–1568)', *Oxford Dictionary of National Biography*, Oxford University Press, 2004; online edn, May 2007 [*http://0-www.oxforddnb.com.lib.exeter.ac.uk/view/article/16867*, accessed 22 Aug 2011]

Kitchener, A. 2001 *Beavers.* Stowmarket, Whittet Books.

Lias, A. 1994 *A Guide to Welsh Place-Names.* Carreg Gwalch, Llanrwst.

Leland, J. 1774 *Antiquarii Collectanea (Collectanea de rebus Britannicus*, tom.iv.*).* London.

Lewis, S. 1985 *A Topographical Dictionary of Wales.* 3rd edition, two vols. Lewis and Co., London.

Lhuyd, E. 1695 *see* Gibson 1695.

Llewelyn Williams, W. 1908 *The Itinerary through Wales, etc, by Giraldus Cambrensis.* London, J. M. Dent and Co.

Lovegrove, R. 2007 *Silent Fields. The long decline of a nation's wildlife.* Oxford, University Press.

Macdonald, D. and Barrett, P. 1993 *Mammals of Britain and Europe.* London, Harper Collins.

Manning, A.D, Bryony J Coles, Angus G Lunn, Duncan J Halley, Philip Ashmole and Stewart J Fallon 2014 New evidence of late survival of beaver in Britain. *The Holocene* published online 26 September 2014.

Marr, M. 2016 Radiocarbon dating of European beaver (*Castor fiber* L. 1958) from Gough's cave provides evidence of population persistence over the Younger Dryas in Britain. *Proc. Univ. Bristol Speleol. Soc.* 27 (1), 105-108.

Meyrick, S.R. 1808 *The History and Antiquities of the County of Cardigan.* London, Longman, Hurst, Rees and Orme.

Monbiot, G. 2013 *Feral.* London, Penguin Books.

Müller-Schwarze, D. and Sun, L. 2003 *The Beaver. Natural History of a Wetlands Engineer.* Ithaca and London, Cornell University Press.

Nayling, N. and Caseldine, A. 1997 *Excavations at Caldicot, Gwent: Bronze Age palaeochannels in the lower Nedern valley.* CBA Research Report 108. York, Council for British Archaeology.

Neill, P. 1819 Proof that the Beaver was formerly a native of Scotland, including an account of some Fossil Remains of that animal found in Perthshire and Berwickshire. *Edinburgh Philosophical Journal* 1, 177-187.

O'Meara, J. J. 1982 *The History and Topography of Ireland by Gerald of Wales*. Harmondsworth, Penguin Books.

Osborne, B.D. 2000 Introduction, in T. Pennant *A Tour in Scotland 1769*, p.ix-xix.

Owen, G. (ed.) 1906 *The description of Pembrokeshire, by George Owen of Henllys*. Part iii. London, Bedford Press.

Owen Pughe, W. 1793 *A Welsh and English Dictionary*. London, E. and T. Williams.

Parry, G. 2004 'Harrison, William (1535–1593)', *Oxford Dictionary of National Biography*, Oxford University Press, 2004 [*http://0-www.oxforddnb.com.lib.exeter.ac.uk/view/article/12453*, accessed 19 May 2011]

Pennant, T. 1771 *A Tour in Scotland 1769*. Chester, John Monk.

Pennant, T. 1774-1776 *A Tour in Scotland, and Voyage to the Hebrides; 1772*. two vols. Chester, John Monk.

Pennant, T. 1776 *British Zoology*. Vol.1. London, Benjamin White.

Pennant, T. 1784 *A Tour in Wales*. London, Benjamin White.

Piggott, S. 1951 William Camden and the *Britannia*. *Proceedings of the British Academy* 37, 199-217.

Piggott, S. 1989 *Ancient Britain and the Antiquarian Imagination*. London, Thames and Hudson.

Radclyffe Dugmore, A. 1914 *The Romance of the Beaver*. London, William Heinemann.

Radclyffe Dugmore, A. 1930 *In the Heart of the Northern Forests*. London, Chatto and Windus.

Ray, J. 1693 *Synopsis Methodica Animalium Quadrupedum et Serpentini Generis*. London, Smith and Walford.

Redknap, M. 1991 Excavation at Newton Moor, South Glamorgan: an interim statement. *Severn Estuary Levels Research Committee Annual Report 1991*, 23-26.

Rhind, P. and Jones, B. 2003 The vegetation history of Snowdonia since the Late Glacial period. *Field Studies* 10, 539-552.

Roberts, Brynley F. 2004 'Lhuyd , Edward (1659/60?–1709)', *Oxford Dictionary of National Biography*, online edn, Oxford University Press, Sept 2004 [*http://0-www.oxforddnb.com.lib.exeter.ac.uk/view/article/16633*, accessed 18 June 2010]

Russell, J. *see* Furnivall 1868.

Rhys, J. 1901 *Celtic Folklore*. Oxford, Clarendon Press.

Seddon, B. 1962 Late-glacial deposits at Llyn Dwythwych and Nant Ffrancon, Caernarvonshire. *Philosophical Transactions of the Royal Society* B 244, 459-481.

Stefen, C. 2009 Intraspecific variability of beaver teeth (Castoridae: Rodentia). *Zoological Journal of the Linnean Society* 155, 926-936.

Thorpe, L. 1978 *Gerald of Wales. The journey through Wales/ The Description of Wales.* Penguin Books, Harmondsworth.

Tree, I. 2018 *Wilding.* London, Picador.

Veale, E. 2003 *The English Fur Trade in the Later Middle Ages.* London Record Society Publications Vol. 38. (Ist edition Oxford University Press 1966)

Walters, G. and Emery, F. 1977 Edward Lhuyd, Edmund Gibson, and the printing of Camden's *Britannia,* 1695. *The Library,* 5th series, Vol. 32 (2), 109-137.

Williams, D.R. 2009 *Edward Lhuyd, 1660-1709. A Shropshire Welshman.* Oswestry, Oswestry and District Civic Society.

Williams, G.J. 2009 Pughe, William Owen (1759-1835), *lexicographer, grammarian, editor, antiquary and poet.* by Emeritus Professor Griffith John Williams, M.A., (1892-1963), Gwaelod-y-garth, Cardiff. Welsh Biography Online. [*http://wbo.llgc.org.uk/en/s-PUGH-OWE-1759.html*, accessed 7 July 2010]

Williams. I.M. (ed.) 2002 *Humphrey Llwyd, Cronica Walliae.* Cardiff, University of Wales Press.

Wilson, C. 1858 Notes on the Prior Existence of the Castor Fiber in Scotland, with its Ancient and Present Distribution in Europe, and on the Use of Castoreum. *The Edinburgh New Philosophical Journal (New Series)* 8, 1-40.

Wilsson, L.1969 *My Beaver Colony.* London, Souvenir Press.

Withers, C.W.J. 1998 Introduction; p. xiii-xxiii in *A Tour in Scotland and Voyage to the Hebrides, 1772, by Thomas Pennant,* ed. A. Simmons. Edinburgh, Birlinn Ltd.

PLACES TO VISIT

BEAVER ENCLOSURES

If you are hoping to see beavers in an enclosure, remember that they are essentially nocturnal and you are unlikely to see them in the daytime. Summer evenings at dusk are usually a good time for seeing them, and it is worth finding out about local beaver-watching sessions. If you visit one of the enclosures during the day, you will most probably be rewarded by signs of beaver activity, which will vary according to the time of year and the character of the locality.

Bevis Trust Website: *www.bevistrust.com*

The BevisTrust is based on a 290 acre farm in Carmarthenshire. There are a number of wildlife projects underway in addition to the beaver enclosures. Contact via the website for details, email *drew@bevistrust.com*, or phone 01267 233 864.

Blaeneinion Currently best to start by going to *https://www.airbnb.co.uk/rooms/1990773* where you will find descriptions of the seventy-five acre site (as well as plenty of information about the B&B side of the enterprise should you need it). Blaeneinion is close to Machynlleth, and to the home of Edward Lhuyd's mother.

Eligro nature reserve, Llangors Website: *www.eligro.uk*

The beaver enclosure lies within a nature reserve on a large arable farm to the south-east of the village (take the B4560 out of the village, and look for a sign on the left to the Multi Activity centre). There are a number of walks which start from the centre, one of which will take you to the beaver enclosure – ask at the centre for advice. Contact via the website, or phone 01874 658 272.

PLACES ASSOCIATED WITH BEAVERS IN THE PAST

Nant Ffrancon OS Map OL 17 covers the relevant area (and a lot more). You could start a visit here at Llyn Ogwen, to look down into the valley. Public transport in the area is very limited, weekends and bank holidays only. There are laybys along the A5, suitable for cars but likely to be full, and there is a pay-and-display car park near Ogwen Cottage, just off the A5 at the west end of Llyn Ogwen. You can ask at Ogwen Cottage (National Trust) about walking down the track into the valley, where about 2.5km down, you can take a public footpath to a footbridge over the Ogwen, a good spot for looking up the river and imagining how it was when beavers lived there. The valley is farmland, so please keep all dogs on the lead, and keep to the track and to public footpaths. The mountains are generally open access, and from Ogwen Cottage you can walk southwards up to Llyn Idwal and Cwm Idwal where Edward Lhuyd went botanising, or eastwards to discover the headwaters of the Llugwy, leading to the Conwy catchment.

Llyn Ebyr and Llyn Dwr Both lakes can be seen from nearby footpaths. The relevant area is covered by OS Maps Landranger 136 and (best for footpaths) Explorer 214. Llyn Ebyr is at SN 9788 and Llyn Dwr at SO 0783.

Cardiff Castle Website: *www.cardiffcastle.com*

The castle, which is in the middle of the city, is open to the public, see website for hours and prices.

No need to wait for dusk here, you will find beavers (but not live ones) in five places, and once you have tracked them down there is much else to see as well. For the beavers, look out for:

- Carved wooden beavers on the 'Stuart' bookcase in the **library** (accessible to all visitors).

- A painted carved stone beaver in stone panels **above the door to the library**, and situated in the **Octagon Staircase**. (Accessible by request to room steward in the library.)

- Carved and painted stone beavers on the chimneypiece of **Lord Bute's Sitting Room** (on the guided tour only).

- The **Roof Garden fountain** – Four beavers included on the bronze fountain, and a beaver on the bronze entrance door. Both by William Burges, c.1877 (on the guided tour only).

INDEX

Avanke, Bever, Castor